# THE DEMENTIA CAREGIVER'S SURVIVAL GUIDE

## AN 11-STEP PLAN TO UNDERSTAND THE DISEASE AND HOW TO COPE WITH FINANCIAL CHALLENGES, PATIENT AGGRESSION, AND DEPRESSION WITHOUT GUILT, OVERWHELM, OR BURNOUT

## JANET G. CRUZ

For permissions requests, speaking inquiries, and bulk order purchase options, email: publishing@uconcept.com.

ISBN: 978-1-960188-02-1 | E-book

ISBN: 978-1-960188-00-7 | Paperback

ISBN: 978-1-960188-01-4 | Hardcover

Published by Unlimited Concepts, Coconut Creek, Florida. www.publishing.u-concept.com

Book, Editing, and Cover Design by UConceptDesigns.com

Published in the United States of America.

# DEDICATION

*I dedicate this book to my beloved family.*

**To my son, Andres.** *There will be no words that could describe how much I love you. You have been my rock during all these years without your father. I have seen you grow to be a responsible, kind, and loving man. I am so proud of you.*

**To my beloved husband, Ray.** *You were and will be the love of my life. I admired you even more through the tough times you had with cancer. You taught me what it means to suffer in silence without losing hope. You were a devoted father who spent every second you had creating memories that shaped our son into such a wonderful human being. I will always love you... Until we meet again....*

**To my beloved mother, Norma**, *who departed too early in her life. You were an example of endurance, love, and faith in the Lord, and carried your cross in silence and humbly. You taught me without* *words how to be the wife and mother I am today; and for that, I will always be grateful. I will always miss you... Until we meet again...*

**To my father, Carlos Enrique.** *We disagree on many things about life, but it doesn't define the bond we feel. Like a phoenix, our love rises from the cinders hot. A bond that has no letters, words nor binds - no matter what we argue about, this love will never truly die. I love you with all my heart.*

**To my brother, Jose Gilberto.** *You and I have a special bond, as close as two siblings could be. We laughed, we played, and sometimes disagree, but the bond between us never seemed to sever. I love you so much and you will always be my true crutch.*

**To my brother, Carlos Jose.** *The oldest of us three. You also departed too soon. I will always love and miss you... Until we meet again...*

# CONTENTS

"There are only four kinds of people in the world. Those who have been caregivers. Those who are currently caregivers. Those who will be caregivers, and those who will need a caregiver."

— Rosalyn Carter

# FOREWORD

By Jose G. Garcia, MD

In "The Dementia Caregiver's Survival Guide", the reader will find all the necessary information to educate and equip a dementia caregiver on how to tackle the very frequently intimidating task of taking care of a dementia patient.

It becomes particularly useful for the regular non-healthcare trained person who suddenly finds him or herself having to take care of a loved one whose intellectual and cognitive abilities are deteriorating and in need of assistance from others for activities of daily life.

It is typically a situation that involves making challenging decisions and often requires making lifestyle changes and adjustments for both the patient and the caregiver.

Through this guide, the reader will gladly discover that he or she is not alone and that there is a significant amount of good advice and available help to make the situation less overwhelming and even make the effort of giving care to a loved one a rewarding activity.

I highly recommend it.

Jose G. Garcia, MD

President and Founder of Rheumatology Center, Inc.

Established Rheumatologic Private Practice in Pembroke Pines, Florida, since 1996

# A Free Gift To Our Readers

30 ready-to-use printable templates you can download to start managing and mindmapping your Caregiver's tasks! Visit:

https://bit.ly/caregivers-action-plan

# LEAVE A 1-CLICK REVIEW

## Customer Reviews

⭐⭐⭐⭐⭐ 2

5.0 out of 5 stars ▾

| | | |
|---|---|---|
| 5 star | ▓▓▓▓▓ | 100% |
| 4 star | | 0% |
| 3 star | | 0% |
| 2 star | | 0% |
| 1 star | | 0% |

See all verified purchase reviews ›

Share your thoughts with other customers

[ Write a customer review ] ⬅

I would be incredibly thankful if you take just 60-seconds to write a brief review on Amazon, even if it's just a few sentences!

https://amazon.com/review/create-review?asin=1960188003

# INTRODUCTION

 "Please remember the real me when I cannot remember you."

– Julie White

Nothing in the world ever prepares us for that life-changing moment when a family member or loved one gets diagnosed with dementia. That single piece of information sends your mind into a state of turmoil where you battle conflicting emotions, including shock, fear, sadness, frustration, and even anger. But still, in the face of this chaos, you have no choice but to assume the role of a dementia caregiver — a long-term job you probably never imagined yourself doing in life. Nevertheless, by accepting to become a caregiver to your dementia parents, family members, or loved ones, you automatically sign up for a new life journey filled with unpredictable, high-stress, emotionally intense, and sometimes rewarding moments.

As caregivers, we often have to give up many aspects of our personal lives to prioritize the needs of our loved ones. The symptoms are usually manageable in the first few months after the diagnosis. However, the story changes as your loved one's condition progress to its later stages. The demand for your assistance increases so fast that in no time, you will constantly be delivering daily 24-hour service to help them complete even the most basic life activities like movement, eating, grooming, shopping, etc. Hence, the time-consuming nature of your caregiving duties forces you to let go of your stress-relieving pursuits and hobbies. In worse cases, even your working hours or the entire job get caught in the sacrifice game. But, as much as it sounds so logical to quit your job to be able to take care of a loved one who truly needs consistent care, the financial burden that comes with caring for a dementia patient puts you at a crossroads.

On one side, you know that quitting your job or reducing your working hours creates an even more enormous strain on the family's finances. But on the other end, you are also aware that not quitting or reducing your work hours may mean that your loved one will have no one to help them survive each day.

In addition to this financial stress and challenging decision-making moments, you also have to adjust to the uncontrollable changes in your relationship dynamics. Whether you are a daughter, wife, sister, or husband to a dementia patient, the circumstances of their condition will push you to take over the position of a parent or higher authority in the relationship. You become the "bigger" person who remains calm, patient, caring, and attentive no matter how increasingly stubborn, violent, or rude the other party becomes on their "bad" days. Of course, this role-switching process sounds relatively straightforward on paper. However, it's usually the most challenging moment for you and your loved ones who might not be willing to accept that they no longer have the authority to play the critical roles they used to in the family. Unfortunately, they tend to express this *unacceptance* through negative emotions that might end up making you feel even more guilty, angry, and frustrated.

Perhaps the peak of the burnout effect develops when you assume that no matter how committed you are to caring for your dementia loved ones, there is only little you can do to stop the deterioration in their physical and mental health. So, as each day passes, you struggle to restore the companionship and emotional connection you once shared with them. You watch helplessly with grief in your heart as your loved one's personality and memories begin to disappear and they transform into a completely different person.

Based on the physical, psychological, and financial burden we have illustrated so far, it is no surprise that recent studies have shown that over 75% of the 16 million dementia caregivers in the U. S. struggle with burnout and emotional distress

(Robinson Wayne and Segal, 2021). Thus, if you fall into this category of caregivers, you need to know that you are neither alone nor are you a wrong person for feeling the way you may be feeling now. On the contrary, you are one of the best people in the world for accepting to take up a role that many people have rejected.

You may wonder why I seem to know so much about what it means and feels like to be a dementia caregiver. The honest answer is that I am one of you. At a very young age, I had to become a caregiver to my beloved aunt, who got diagnosed with dementia. The journey was challenging because, like you, I had zero experience. My naivety and the lack of assistance from other family members only worsened matters. I had to figure out how to deal with the aggressiveness and other behavioral changes that my aunty constantly exhibited, even when I desperately tried to help her. And before I knew it, I started experiencing the caregiver's burnout effect in its full fold. I found it hard to sleep or eat even when I was so tired and hungry. As such, I got easily irritated. Eventually, all the signs summed up to depression, and it was at that point I realized that I had to find the right kind of help. Although it took time, I finally got the breakthrough I desperately needed. This break-through helped set me free from emotional distress and made me an even better caregiver to my aunt.

My years of struggle as a dementia caregiver and eventual triumph pushed me to create the masterpiece you now have in your hands. Before my breakthrough, I promised myself that if I ever made it through my dark days, I would spend my entire life ensuring that fewer people go through the same dark experiences I encountered while caring for my loved one. As such, I combined my caregiving experiences with my studies in Psychology and Sociology to be a better dementia caregiver and now I share my knowledge and experiences with those who may also be struggling with the caregiving burnout effects.

Through my experiences with caregivers, I discovered that most of us often struggle to cope with the difficulties posed by our dementia loved ones because we lack the foundational awareness about their condition. Remember, we never prepared for this job but took it up boldly with zero experience or idea of what it truly entails.

Sadly, there are only a few resources available to gain the adequate understanding that we need to become the best support system for our loved ones without losing our minds at any point. But the reality is about to change for the better, for this book will become your knight in shining armor through whom you will learn how to navigate this path of dementia caregiving properly.

We will start by first understanding the basics of dementia, from its causes and symptoms to its different types and possible medical treatments. If you are worried that our discussions on these topics will resemble a biology class, let me reassure you that it will be nothing like that. Instead, we will break down these medical concepts to the simplest form using illustrations from the life experiences of several caregivers who have walked through the same journey you are currently on or are about to start.

Once we have set up that foundation correctly, we will move into the core aspects of an ideal caregiving journey. At this point, we will explore the world of your dementia loved ones to help you understand firsthand their condition, feelings, and reasonings from their perspective. From that point, we will switch into a full self-reflection mode, where you will learn how to truly understand and address your feelings, emotions, and thoughts as a caregiver. During this process, you will determine the leading causes of your burnout and the best strategies to overcome those factors.

Having understood these two critical perspectives, we will move on to our next task, which involves developing an effective action plan to ensure your loved one receives the optimal level of care and attention that he/she deserves without neglecting your physical and mental wellness. In addition to this effective action plan we will be designing, you also need as much support and help as possible. As such, the book offers a bonus chapter where we identify and analyze reliable resource areas from which you can get adequate physical, mental, and financial support.

No matter how severe the condition of your loved one is, being a dementia caregiver to them does not have to be a traumatic experience. You deserve to enjoy the remarkable and fulfilling side of dementia caregiving more often despite its inevitable challenges. And this book is your key to achieving that incredible breakthrough.

Right now, I cannot wait to start this journey, which will undoubtedly be life-changing for you and me. So, shall we begin this adventure?

# UNDERSTANDING DEMENTIA

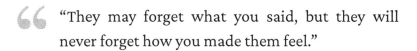

"They may forget what you said, but they will never forget how you made them feel."

– Carl W. Buechner

*A*ccording to the U. S. Centers for Disease Control, over 5 million older adults have been diagnosed with dementia as of 2020. Medical experts and scientists even projected that by 2050, the number would have risen to 13.8 million.

Unsurprisingly, these alarming statistics tend to strike justifiable fear in our minds as we age. Moreover, such fear sometimes breeds different misconceptions about dementia. Hence, today, most of us have more awareness about the myths of dementia rather than the actual truths and realities of the condition. Nevertheless, our goal in this chapter is to debunk those myths and uncover the fundamental truths of everything dementia involves as a medical condition. So, shall we begin?

## WHAT IS DEMENTIA?

The first thing we need to understand about dementia is that it is not one disease. Instead, it is a syndrome that leads to the deterioration of a person's cognitive function to the point where it interferes negatively with their daily lifestyle and social interaction. By a person's cognitive functioning, we mean their mental abilities of learning, thinking, remembering, processing thoughts, solving problems, and making decisions. These cognitive skills are undoubtedly invaluable, as they influence critical parts of our daily lives. As such, in the case of dementia patients, the deteriorated state of their mental skills makes it almost impossible for them to work through their daily lives smoothly and independently. Nevertheless, despite the alarming increase in dementia cases in the 21st century, not every age group is susceptible to it. The condition is most prevalent among older adults in their 60s and above.

Because of these age peculiarities shared by dementia patients, some people tend to assume that dementia is an inevitable development resulting from aging. However, this assumption is very wrong. The fact that dementia is quite prevalent in aged adults does not make it a natural or inevitable part of aging. Of course, most humans experience a gradual decrease in the quality of their short-term memory as they age. However, such a decrease is slight compared to the case of dementia. Besides, we should remember that memory deterioration or loss is not the only mental impairment that characterizes this condition.

Later in the chapter, we will clarify beyond reasonable doubt that aging is not responsible for the development of dementia in older adults. However, let's first explore the medically and scientifically proven causes of this condition.

## WHAT CAUSES DEMENTIA?

Do you remember we said earlier that dementia is not a specific disease but a syndrome of various conditions? This definition implies that dementia occurs in different types, and each type of dementia has its distinct pathology (Newman, 2020). Nonetheless, they all share one general cause: the disruption or damage of the brain cells, specifically in the cerebral cortex, the brain region responsible for thinking, learning, memory, problem-solving, and other cognitive functions.

Perhaps you now understand why we said earlier that dementia leads to the deterioration of a person's cognitive functioning abilities. However, the disruption or damage to the brain cells in the cerebral cortex is not always permanent in all types of dementia. There are cases where proper medical treatment can be employed to slow and cure the disruption or damage. We refer to such types of dementia as reversible dementia. They include Delirium, Wernicke-Korsakoff Syndrome, and Normal Pressure Hydrocephalus.

Research studies have shown that irreversible types of dementia are the leading cause of the alarming increase in dementia cases today. Chapter 2 will discuss all 10 types of dementia, but for now, let's focus on analyzing the three most common dementia types and their specific causes.

- **Alzheimer's Disease**

Alzheimer's disease accounts for 60 to 70 percent of dementia cases today (Newman, 2020). It is so common that people wrongly assume it is the only type of dementia. Notwithstanding, Alzheimer's disease is primarily caused by the abnormal accumulation of a toxic protein type called *Beta amyloids* and *tau*, another protein collected inside the brain neurons. These two proteins continually accumulate in the cerebral cortex until they kill the cells in that brain region (National Institute on Aging, 2017).

The death of the brain cells in that brain region leads to the development of Alzheimer's disease. This buildup, however, does not happen in a night. It takes about 10 to 20 years for the accumulation to reach a point where an aged person showcases symptoms of Alzheimer's disease. Thus, we can now see that age is a high-risk factor for developing Alzheimer's disease. However, the accumulated Beta amyloids and tau do not stop at the cerebral cortex. Over time, they also destroy other areas of the brain, which causes the affected patient to lose their ability to function and live independently.

- **Vascular Dementia**

Vascular dementia comes right after Alzheimer's disease as the second leading cause of dementia. However, these two dementia types differ in different aspects. As its name implies, vascular dementia is linked to cardiovascular illnesses such as heart disease, hypertension, diabetes, and other illnesses that impact the flow of blood. For this reason, aged adults with a previous history of these conditions are said to be more susceptible to this type of dementia.

So, what leads to the development of vascular dementia? Its story begins when fatty deposits accumulate around the brain arteries' walls to an abnormal level, restricting blood flow to critical brain parts, including the cerebral cortex. By limiting blood flow, the accumulated fatty deposits, also known as atherosclerosis, deprive the brain cells and tissues of oxygen. And this deprivation will eventually lead to their death. Since the individual occurrence of restricted blood flow and cessation of brain tissue mostly goes unnoticed, the damage builds up over time within the cognitive region of the brain.

Eventually, the person experiencing vascular dementia will exhibit visible signs of the condition, such as deteriorating cognitive abilities and speech impairments.

- **Parkinson's Disease**

Though scientific researchers have not identified the specific cause of this dementia type, they discovered that its development is associated with the disruption and damage of nerve cells in the *substantia nigra* structure of the brain (Dementia.org, 2020). This part of the brain is specifically responsible for producing dopamine, a hormone that controls the body's movement and the brain's chemical signaling to its different parts. Hence, by damaging the nerve cells in that brain region, Parkinson's disease causes a significant reduction in dopamine production, inhibiting the brain from sending the right signals to its different sections and affecting the body's movements. Thus, affected patients of Parkinson's disease often experience deteriorations in their mobility and cognitive functioning.

## IS DEMENTIA A GENETIC CONDITION?

Though we now know the general cause of dementia and the individual causes of its three most common types, the question of its genetic susceptibility remains unclear. Unlike the popular myth that dementia is purely genetic, research studies have proven that most dementia cases are not inheritable (Newman, 2020). Nonetheless, they still discovered certain unusual instances in which genetics can have strong links to a person's development of dementia.

For example, when a person develops a rare case of Alzheimer's disease in their 30s and 40s, there is a higher chance that the person has acquired a faulty gene from their parents that is capable of being transmitted to the next generation. This particular case is known as *Young-onset Familial Alzheimer's Disease* (Alzheimer's Society, 2021). Nevertheless, we must note that it only occurs in a tiny proportion of cases – about 1 in every 33 people develops Alzheimer's disease before they reach their 60s. Ultimately, children and grandchildren of aged dementia patients cannot inherit the condition under normal circumstances. However, in rare cases of Young-onset Familial Alzheimer's Disease, the possibility of genetic transmission is very high.

NORMAL AGING VS. DEMENTIA

Earlier in this chapter, we established that memory deterioration is often the most common aging symptom that people relate to dementia. However, several other aging symptoms, like planning and decision problems, language difficulties, mood, and behavioral changes, also fall into this category. So let's analyze these symptoms and establish what constitutes normal aging and what does not.

- **Memory Deterioration**

The normal aging process slows down the brain's information-processing ability. As such, almost 40 percent of adults over 60 in the U. S. encounter occasional lapses of mild forgetfulness (Marill, 2022). We say this type of forgetfulness is benign because it does not cause any impairment in your daily life.

For example, an older adult can occasionally forget details of previous conversations, names of old acquaintances, or the location of their belongings like car keys, phone, or glasses. But they always figure it out later. You would agree that such momentary lapses are too mild to stop anyone from completing their daily tasks. However, the signs of memory deterioration from dementia are so intense that it's difficult for those who suffer from it to manage their daily lives and be independent.

A glaring contrast between age-related memory loss and dementia is that the latter restricts a person's ability to learn and retain new information. An example is when older adults keep forgetting things you tell them some seconds before, and they repeatedly ask for that same information. They quickly lose track of dates and times and even find it hard to operate appliances. In most cases, dementia patients are often unaware of their memory problem, but it is always self-evident to close relatives and friends. It is essential to note that in between typical age-related memory impairment and dementia, we have a condition known as Mild Cognitive Impairment or MCI (Alzheimer Society of Canada, 2020). Its symptoms include mild memory loss, speech difficulties, and visual disorientation. Studies have shown that MCI is a precursor with a high chance of developing Alzheimer's disease.

- **Planning and Decision Problems**

Ideally, people gain more life experiences and lessons when they age, enabling them to become better planners and decision-makers. However, since aging significantly affects the brain's information processing speed, older adults struggle to think through things thoroughly and quickly. Hence, they take longer to plan things and sometimes make hasty decisions without thinking them through. So, you might witness your older loved one making slight mistakes while paying their bills or managing their budgets. However, these mistakes never lead to severe consequences. Also, most aged adults struggle with multitasking, but they can easily achieve tasks when honing in on only one task at a time. In contrast, dementia impairs people's ability to perform multiple tasks simultaneously and even to concentrate on a single task. As such, they need help to plan appropriately or make an informed decision. Before they even get halfway through a decision-making process, their minds get confused. Thus, they need help to perform tasks like following a recipe, paying bills, or making lists for grocery shopping.

- **Language and Conversation Difficulties**

Due to age-induced memory deterioration, some older adults struggle with their language skills, especially vocabulary. They sometimes cannot find the right words to express themselves, but they mostly end up remembering. Additionally, they

JANET G. CRUZ

quickly get distracted during their conversations with others because they need a higher concentration level to keep up with what the other party says (Alzheimer's Society, 2022). It becomes even more difficult for them to focus when they have different people talking to them simultaneously. However, even without distraction, older adults with dementia still find it challenging to engage in conversations properly and not lose track of what the other person is saying. Also, while normal aging makes one occasionally and temporarily forget the right words to use in their interactions, dementia patients experience this problem more often than usual. They need assistance finding the right words to say.

- **Mood and Behavioral Changes**

Normal aging often leads to significant emotional changes, which causes gradual altercations in older adults' behavioral patterns. Sometimes, these changes could result from the side effects of their medications. Studies show that older adults fill an average of 14 to 18 prescriptions yearly (Hightower, 2020). These medications tend to induce symptoms like occasional and short-term tiredness, anxiety, restlessness, irritation, or impulsiveness, which might influence the mood of concerned persons. It could also be because of depression and other mental health issues, which are pretty standard among aged people in the 21st century.

Mood and behavioral changes are also prevalent in dementia patients, but the significant differentiating factor is that these changes continue for longer. For example, these mood and behavioral changes might cause your loved one to lose interest altogether and withdraw entirely from family gatherings. Ultimately, aging rarely causes violence and aggressiveness, but these two top the list of behaviors quickly noticed in people living with dementia.

## EARLY SIGNS OF DEMENTIA

We have proven beyond reasonable doubt that dementia is not a natural aging process, though its occurrence is prevalent in older adults. Let's now explore more noticeable warning signs and symptoms that can help you quickly detect if your loved one has dementia.

Some warning symptoms you can look out for:

- They constantly have trouble remembering recent and familiar things like the names and faces of close relatives, how to perform simple and regular tasks or the reasons for their actions.

- Occasionally, you may find your loved one in a state of confusion, unable to recall the reasoning behind their actions. In most cases, they need help to remember.

- They continue inquiring about matters which they are already familiar with.

- Their gradual memory impairment makes them unable to complete simple and familiar tasks they used to do independently.

- They suddenly become apathetic and disinterested in activities and hobbies from which they used to derive great pleasure.

- They quickly lose track of what day it is or the routes to familiar places. So, they often get lost on their streets, on their way to the grocery store, or even at home.

- They exhibit severe changes in their mood and behaviors for no apparent reason. For example, your loved one might gradually become anxious, easily irritated, aggressive, and withdrawn.

- Their sense of judgment deteriorates, and you see them making moves out of character, like wearing thick clothes during summer or taking things from the trash bin.

- They are not able to accomplish tasks that involve abstract thinking or calculations, such as reconciling checkbooks, paying bills, managing finances, completing forms, or understanding instructions.

## IMPORTANCE AND BENEFITS OF AN EARLY DEMENTIA DIAGNOSIS

Although we did great by identifying the early symptoms that help a person determine if they have dementia, we cannot deny that being told you have dementia is a frightening experience for anyone. This reality explains why many older adults hide their suspected symptoms and behavioral changes from their loved ones for as long as possible. However, such actions cause more harm and prevent patients from experiencing the vital advantages that early detection of dementia can bring to their psychological and physical health.

Early diagnosis enables dementia patients to get immediate and timely medical care. Since there is currently no cure for dementia, drugs serve as a better alternative, as they help stabilize and delay the cognitive decline that dementia causes in the brain. Thus, by getting an early diagnosis, your loved one can enjoy the best benefits of these medications at a very early stage in the syndrome's development process. At that stage, it is easier to manage both the simple and severe symptoms that characterize the condition. Proper management helps ensure that your loved one maintains a healthy quality of life with the preservation of cognitive abilities.

An early diagnosis also gives you, as a caregiver, and your loved one, adequate time to better understand everything about the condition. By becoming more knowledgeable about the specific dementia type affecting your loved one, you can assist them in making informed and educated decisions concerning their health. Most importantly, it will help you know how to provide them with the proper support.

## CAN DEMENTIA BE PREVENTED?

Medical experts and researchers have yet to develop scientifically proven medications or measures to completely prevent people, especially older adults, from developing dementia. Nevertheless, they have conducted a significant number of successful clinical trials which prove that all types of dementia are preventable to some extent. Now, the big question is, what steps do we take to prevent the onset of dementia?

Every type of dementia has risk factors that increase its chances of progression. Thus, if you want to protect your older parents and family members from developing dementia, you need to identify and reduce the effectiveness of those risk factors to the barest minimum.

## WHAT ARE THE RISK FACTORS OF DEMENTIA?

Just like its causes and symptoms, the risk factors of dementia may differ from one type to the next. However, all dementia types have general risk factors that they commonly share. Some of them include the following:

- **Age and Genes:** In the first part of this chapter, we already established how these two factors play significant roles in the brain's development of dementia. Although age is best known as the most prevalent risk factor, genetics only contributes to dementia development in rare cases of Young-onset Familial Alzheimer's Disease.

- **Diabetes:** Diabetes is a health condition caused by high sugar levels. Thus, when patients do not properly manage it, the excess sugar increases in the body and damages different body organs, including the brain cells. With such disruption, it becomes easier for the onset of dementia, especially Alzheimer's disease. Research studies show a strong link between type 2 diabetes and Alzheimer's disease (Budson, 2021).

- **High Blood Pressure:** This risk factor is mainly connected to vascular dementia. It causes damage to the brain, heart, and blood vessels (Alzheimers.gov, 2022), thus making it easier for fatty tissues to build up around the arteries and stop blood and oxygen circulation.

- **Environmental Factors:** Other important environmental factors that can increase the risk of dementia onset include high alcohol intake, smoking, hearing loss, untreated depression, lack of exercise, increased loneliness, and social isolation (NHS, 2020).

## HOW TO REDUCE THE RISK OF DEMENTIA

Reducing the risk of factors like age and genes is impossible because they are beyond our control. However, there are several effective lifestyle changes that older adults - whether or not they are living with dementia - can still incorporate into their daily reality to lower the risk of developing dementia or slow down the progression of their cognitive decline. They should:

- Attend regular checkups or screening appointments with healthcare providers, whether or not they have chronic health conditions.

- Maintain high physical activity by adopting a moderate-intensity workout routine and sticking to it.

- Constantly engage in activities and hobbies that improve their mental alertness. It could be reading books, solving puzzles, playing games or sports, traveling, volunteering, or even crafting things with their hands.

- Eat healthy balanced diets and limit fat and sugar intake.

- Get adequate sleep time, ideally between seven to eight hours every night.

- Abstain entirely from smoking and lower alcohol intake to the barest minimum. Doing so makes older adults less susceptible to falls and reduces the risk of developing cardiovascular diseases, all precursors of dementia.

- Increase social interaction by regularly attending social events and engaging in social activities will help them feel less lonely or isolated.

So far, we have uncovered the truth behind dementia while debunking any misunderstandings regarding its origins, signs and symptoms, ways to reduce one's risk of developing it, and preventative measures. So, let's move to the next chapter, where we shall examine, more broadly, the different dementia types that exist in the 21st century.

# TYPES OF DEMENTIA

> "Kindness can transform someone's dark moment with a blaze of light. You'll never know how much your caring matters."
>
> – Amy Leigh Mercree

In the previous chapter, we already established that, contrary to the common misconception, there are many dementia types, each of which has unique peculiarities. While we previously only considered the three most common dementia types and their differences in terms of causes, this chapter involves a more detailed analysis of ten different types of dementia.

We'll explore everything there is to know about them, including the causes and symptoms, risk factors, and available treatment options. So if you ever thought that all dementia types are the same, get ready to unlearn those incorrect assumptions!

## ALZHEIMER'S DISEASE

From our previous discussion, you already know that Alzheimer's disease is the most common type of dementia and that it accounts for about 60 to 70 percent of dementia cases in the U. S. But despite these high statistics, you should not try to generalize it as the only existing dementia type. Alzheimer's is specifically a *progressive* brain disease (Mayo Clinic, 2021).

Let's break down what makes Alzheimer's a progressive brain disease. Firstly, progressive means that Alzheimer's develops at a *gradual* pace. In fact, research studies have proven that it takes 10 to 20 years for its symptoms to start surfacing. It's easier to understand why this development takes so long if you understand its primary cause.

The development begins when two toxic proteins (Amyloids beta and tau) are deposited into the cerebral cortex, a critical brain region, until they accumulate to an abnormal level. The accumulated protein deposits form into plaques and tangles at this abnormal level. While the tangles twist together to kill the brain cells in the cortex region, the plaques block and break the connections between the brain cells and neurons. As more healthy brain cells continue to die, the brain continuously and significantly shrinks to its worst state (Yetman, 2021). Though it sounds pretty simple when written down, the abnormal accumulation of these toxic proteins takes a long and complicated process. So, how do you know that your loved one explicitly has Alzheimer's disease? This part is quite tricky, as the symptoms of Alzheimer's could overlap with that of other dementia types at some point. However, we already know that Alzheimer's disease affects the cerebral cortex, the brain area mainly responsible for learning and memory. Thus, studies have shown that its early signs mostly center on a person's ability to learn, retain, and remember new or familiar information (Alzheimer's Association, 2021).

As the disease advances, the symptoms also get severe. Your loved one might exhibit signs like disorientation, impaired judgment, depression, anxiety, and other behavioral changes. Eventually, in the later stages of the disease, it becomes difficult for them to talk, walk, or eat independently. At the moment, Alzheimer's disease is still a terminal disease with no cure. However, early diagnosis can become a saving grace as it allows every patient to slow the progression of their condition.

## VASCULAR DEMENTIA

Vascular dementia is the second most frequent form of dementia in the United States, making up approximately 5-10% of all reported cases. In other words, one in every ten dementia patients has this specific type of dementia. However, vascular dementia is quite different from Alzheimer's disease despite the popularity they both share. Unlike the protein build-up associated with Alzheimer's, the development of vascular dementia involves the blockage of blood flow to the brain. Let's simplify it, shall we?

Every human has specific body components called arteries, responsible for supplying blood to the brain through cerebral circulation (Kinman, 2016). This supplied blood usually contains oxygen, glucose, and other nutrients with which the brain derives energy to carry out its cognitive functions of reasoning and thinking. However, in vascular dementia, cerebral circulation gets impaired because of the blockage of the blood-supplying arteries. Since there is no artery to enable the free flow of the brain, the brain automatically gets deprived of oxygen and other essential nutrients.

In the previous chapter, we mentioned that vascular dementia is closely linked to heart-related health conditions such as stroke, high blood pressure, and diabetes. This association is because these conditions have a high potential for damaging blood vessels and blocking the brain's arteries. Thus, we can lower the risk of vascular dementia by controlling these conditions. Nonetheless, the earliest and most significant symptoms you will notice if your loved one has vascular dementia have nothing to do with memory loss like Alzheimer's. Instead, it mainly involves a significant decline in their reasoning and overall thinking process. So you notice them struggling to make simple decisions, concentrate or organize their actions or thoughts. In the case of vascular dementia that develops suddenly after a stroke, the person's movement ability also gets affected. Still, it is always possible for vascular dementia patients to develop similar symptoms to Alzheimer's in the later stages of their condition.

## LEWY BODY DEMENTIA (LBD)

This particular type of dementia is similar to Alzheimer's disease in two significant ways. First, it is a progressive brain disease, and its cause is also associated with the accumulation of protein deposits. However, with Lewy body dementia, the protein *alpha-synuclein* accumulates in the brain's nerve cells (Mayo Clinic, 2021). When the accumulation reaches abnormal levels, it becomes Lewy bodies.

The brain region where these nerve cells are located controls mental abilities, such as movement, memory, vision, and thinking. As such, the presence of the Lewy bodies in that area leads to the loss of specific important neurons that are important for transmitting two of the most crucial body hormones – *acetylcholine* and *dopamine*. While acetylcholine centers on learning and control, dopamine functions as the messenger, transmitting information to the nerve cells that control movement, sleep, and mood. By reducing the levels at which these hormones are produced, the Lewy bodies cause a gradual deterioration of the mental operations that those nerve cells control. Visual hallucination is one significant symptom that over 80 percent of people living with LBD tend to showcase right from the early stage of their condition (National Institute on Aging, 2021).

You might notice your loved one constantly claiming to see people or objects that are not present. In rare cases, the hallucination could be non-visual, where they hear and smell things that aren't present in their surroundings. Along with visual hallucination, LBD patients also exhibit signs like unpredictable changes in their focus and attention level, disorientation about time and place, language difficulties, and impaired judgment at the early stage of their disease.

Sometimes, LBD patients may also experience movement problems at this early stage. However, in most cases, it takes a few years of the disease's progression before anyone living with LBD begins to show any mobility-related symptoms. Notwithstanding, these movement problems usually begin with immense stiffness in their muscles, thus making them unable to walk correctly. Instead, they shuffle-walk at a languid pace and with a stooped posture (National Institute on Aging, 2021). They also experience repeated falls because of their balance and coordination problems. As time passes, the muscles in their hands and face also get affected, and you might see an unusual but sudden change in their handwriting. And, because their facial muscles are so stiff, it becomes harder for them to make the correct facial expressions when communicating.

The later stages of this disease get worse as the patient exhibits severe symptoms like sleeping disorder, sexual dysfunction, dizziness, and intense aggressiveness, which develop from delusions and paranoia, depression, and anxiety. Nonetheless, like the other dementia types we have examined, there is no particular medical cure for LBD. However, clinical studies have revealed that medications and other types of therapies can help some of its acute symptoms (National Institute on Aging, 2021).

## PARKINSON'S DISEASE

This dementia type shares many similarities with Lewy body dementia regarding its causes and symptoms. Like in LBD, Parkinson's disease is caused by a significant reduction in dopamine production because of the continuous death of cells in the *substantia nigra*, another critical brain area. The absence of enough dopamine makes it difficult for the part of the brain that controls body movement to function correctly (Moore, 2021). As such, the most noticeable symptoms of Parkinson's disease center on movement. These movement problems are almost the same as the ones experienced in the later stages of Lewy body dementia. Nonetheless, the signs of Parkinson's disease begin to surface with intense muscle rigidness in any part of the body, from the face to the legs. This rigidity slows their movement pace when doing even the simplest tasks, like eating. They also shuffle-walk while falling repeatedly and without being able to swing their arms as freely as they used to.

As the illness advances, people living with Parkinson's disease start to experience tremors in their jaw, lips, hands, legs, and even the tongue when these body parts are not in use. These tremors affect their speaking and writing ability, thus causing them to have a weak and monotone voice and smaller hand-writing.

You have probably noticed that we have not mentioned any cognitive-related symptoms so far. Well, that omission is because the disease's early stages only affect movement. However, the late stages of the disease involve more complications. Patients will experience additional cognitive difficulties, such as depression, emotional and behavioral changes, smell and sexual dysfunction, delusions, and bladder problems.

## HUNTINGTON'S DISEASE

Do you remember what we said in the last chapter about dementia being genetic? Well, Alzheimer's disease is not the only inheritable dementia type. This dementia type also belongs to the category but is just as rare as Alzheimer's disease (Mayo Clinic, 2021). So, where does its story begin?

Scientific researchers traced the cause of Huntington's disease to a defective gene passed down to a person by their parents. Thus, right from birth, this faulty gene appears in some parts of the brain and gradually damages the nerve cells in those regions (Alzheimer's Society, 2021). This damage affects a patient's functional abilities, thus causing them to develop cognitive (mental), psychiatric (behavioral), and mobility (physical) disorders.

What differentiates this dementia type from others is that age is not a high-risk factor. Studies have confirmed that people can develop Huntington's disease at any age (NHS, 2021). It could be as early as age two and as late as age eighty. Nevertheless, most people with Huntington's disease begin to show symptoms in their early 30s and 40s. However, it becomes a case of Juvenile Huntington's disease if the symptoms surface when the patient is below the age of twenty.

Though the development of Huntington's disease in younger people differs from that of older humans, they share the same symptoms. So, what are the symptoms of Huntington's disease? Its physical symptoms include immense weight loss, muscle stiffness, impaired coordination and balance, unusual eye movement, and speech difficulties. However, the cognitive symptoms range from concentration and memory problems to the inability to control themselves.

According to medical experts, depression is the leading psychiatric symptom experienced by people with Huntington's disease. Other conditions, like insomnia, social withdrawal, suicidal thoughts, and anxiety, accompany it. In rare cases, the psychiatric symptoms worsen to the point of obsessive-compulsive disorder and bipolar disorder.

Ultimately, people with a family history of Huntington's disease are the most susceptible to this type of dementia. Thus, the best preventive option is to subject themselves to genetic testing to be adequately informed about whether or not they have a high risk of developing this condition. Remember that early diagnosis is the most effective way to manage any dementia type, so go!

## CREUTZFELDT-JAKOB DISEASE (CJD)

This type of dementia is just as complicated and scary as its name. According to medical experts, Creutzfeldt-Jakob disease damages the brain cells at an even faster rate than Alzheimer's disease. Its development begins when a group of faulty proteins, also known as *prions*, accumulate in the brain cells to the point where they damage these cells and make the brain look like a sea sponge with holes everywhere.

Eighty to ninety percent of CJD cases have unknown sources. However, research studies have shown that 10 to 15 percent of them are usually acquired through verified means, such as getting in touch with a contaminated surgical apparatus or inheriting a faulty gene from their parents. One could also acquire it by eating beef from cows who suffered from *bovine spongiform encephalopathy* (BSE), another infection caused by prions. By eating beef from an infected cow, the faulty proteins get transferred into the person's body system.

It normally takes around 8 to 10 years before dementia symptoms begin to surface. However, it's a different story with CJD. After the affected person gets the disease, it only takes months and, in rare cases, a few years for the symptoms to surface. The initial indicators of CJD resemble those of Alzheimer's disease; symptoms such as cognitive decline, loss of recollection and orientation, and transformation in behavior. However, as the disease worsens, symptoms similar to Lewy body dementia, like visual hallucinations, muscle and balance coordination, and uncontrollable tremors, also begin to appear. In the late stages of the disease, CJD patients experience seizures, paralysis, and immense loss of weight and muscle mass.

Unlike other types of dementia, whose progression we can slow down with proper treatment, there is currently no proven way to manage the worsening effects of Creutzfeldt-Jakob disease. However, the good news is that CJD is a rare type of dementia. According to the United States Centers for Disease Control, only about 350 people are diagnosed with CJD in the U. S. yearly. In typical cases, CJD primarily affects older adults in their 50s, 60s, and above. Ultimately, the truth remains that no matter how fatal this condition is, early diagnosis can still go a long way in helping affected persons live healthier lives.

FRONTOTEMPORAL DEMENTIA

This type of dementia often gets mistaken for advanced Alzheimer's disease and even with a psychiatric problem. It is pretty easy to make such mistakes because frontotemporal dementia is caused by the atrophy (shrinking) of both frontal and temporal lobes in the brain. (Mayo Clinic, 2021). These brain areas control a person's language ability, personality, and behavior. As such, when these lobes shrink, the affected individuals exhibit sudden and dramatic changes in their personalities or a deterioration in their ability to interact appropriately with others or use language correctly. They also experience movement-related problems like muscle weakness and spasms, tremors, constant falls, and the inability to show proper facial expression due to their stiff facial muscles.

To a large extent, age is not a high-risk factor for frontotemporal dementia, as it primarily affects adults between the ages of 40 and 60. However, people with an extended family history of frontotemporal dementia have a higher risk of getting the disease.

## NORMAL PRESSURE HYDROCEPHALUS (NPH)

Just like how blood flows into the brain to provide oxygen and nutrients to its different components, another important fluid substance known as the *cerebrospinal fluid* (CSF) also flows throughout the brain and spinal cord (National Institute of Neurological Disorders and Stroke, 2021). However, Normal Pressure Hydrocephalus develops when excess cerebrospinal fluid accumulates abnormally in the brain's ventricles. With every excess CSF that gets dumped in brain ventricles, its chambers get more enlarged, and eventually, they disrupt and damage the brain cells around the ventricles.

This damage leads to several cognitive and movement-related problems, such as walking difficulties, impaired judgment and decision-making, slow thinking, and apathetic behaviors towards things and activities they used to love. In the later stages of the illness, an affected individual might experience a loss of bladder control. Nevertheless, the most extraordinary thing about this type of dementia is that it is curable to a large extent. Isn't that incredible? Yes! If your loved one has Normal Pressure Hydrocephalus, they can get treated through a surgical operation in which the excess CSF gets drained out from the brain. With that removal, the surgery helps in solving movement-related problems. However, research studies have shown that the surgery has not been effective in correcting the symptoms relating to cognitive functioning. Still, we should not get discouraged. Who knows if the surgery could become even more effective in the future?

## WERNICKE-KORSAKOFF SYNDROME

This dementia type occurs mainly as a result of Vitamin B1 deficiency. Vitamin B1 is an essential nutrient to the brain, as it is an excellent energy source. Thus, a severe lack of this nutrient causes significant damage to the brain cells.

People with poor nutrition and those who consume unhealthy amounts of alcohol are the most vulnerable to this type of dementia. Though it also affects older adults with prior cases of bowel and stomach diseases. But how do you know if your loved one shows signs of Wernicke-Korsakoff syndrome? Its early symptoms include vision problems, disorientation about time and place, and balance and coordination problems during movement. However, as the disease becomes long-term, the symptoms worsen into severe amnesia, a confused mental state, and hallucinations.

Although there is no cure for Wernicke-Korsakoff Syndrome, medical professionals can help delay or even stop its progression if the disease gets diagnosed early and treatment is administered promptly.

## MIXED DEMENTIA

As its name implies, mixed dementia is a condition that develops when a person showcases apparent clinical symptoms and features of at least two different dementia types (Alzheimer's Society, 2021). Studies have revealed that this type of dementia primarily affects the oldest patients, especially those in their late 70s and 80s.

Generally, people with mixed dementia exhibit varying symptoms depending on the dementia types that contribute to their condition. The most common types of mixed dementia include Alzheimer's disease & vascular dementia, and Alzheimer's disease & Lewy body dementia. In most diagnoses of mixed dementia, one dementia type is always more predominant than the other, so the affected person experiences a greater volume of one dementia type than the other.

Perhaps you are suspicious that your loved one is experiencing mixed dementia. All you have to do is list all the noticeable signs you see and compare them to the symptoms of

Alzheimer's disease, vascular dementia, and Lewy body dementia we examined in this chapter.

To wrap up this chapter, we must understand that diagnosing any dementia is not as easy as it seems on paper. Based on what we have discussed so far, you probably agree that the symptoms of the different dementia types tend to overlap at some point. Thus, your healthcare expert remains the best to seek when you want the right and precise diagnosis of your loved one's dementia type.

# THE 7 STAGES OF DEMENTIA

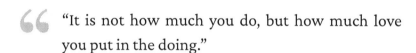

"It is not how much you do, but how much love you put in the doing."

– Mother Teresa

*A*fter exploring in Chapter 2 the various dementia types, including Creutzfeldt-Jakob disease, which can develop rapidly, you probably noticed they all share a common characteristic: *progressiveness*. This progressive (gradual) factor implies that dementia does not develop into advanced stages in just a few days. Instead, it progresses through a gradual decline in which the symptoms and needs of your loved one change as time passes. Thus, to make our jobs as caregivers easier, medical experts and scientists designed an incredible model that illustrates the progression of cognitive decline in people with dementia through seven critical stages. For each of the seven dementia stages, the signs, symptoms, and treatment options differ. And, by understanding as a caregiver what each dementia stage entails, you'll be able to discern through careful assessment your loved one's current stage of illness, allowing for more accurate treatment.

With an accurate identification, your job becomes easier as you understand how to offer the support your loved one truly needs at every stage. Additionally, it will help you make effective plans to cater to his/her future needs. Besides improving your role as a caregiver, understanding the current stage of your beloved's condition can make a significant difference in delaying the progress of their cognitive decline.

Now that you know the life-changing benefits that emerge from understanding the seven stages of dementia, let us analyze each stage and see what they entail in terms of symptoms, mode of diagnosis, treatment options, and the patient's needs.

## STAGE 1: NO COGNITIVE DECLINE

In the first stage of dementia, your loved ones do not show any visible signs that can be associated with any brain disease. However, the non-visibility of its symptoms does not translate to the non-existence of the disease. At this point, the disease is already present in their brains. However, it is silently developing by damaging and killing more brain cells. But, despite the gradual destruction in their brains, your loved one behaves normally and easily navigates through their daily life with no negative effects and interference.

Usually, transitioning to the second stage could take a few months or several years, depending on the type of dementia involved. So, for example, if your loved one has Alzheimer's disease, which has a very slow progression rate, their 'no cognitive decline' stage could last for ten to twenty years. However, with quick progressive dementias like Creutzfeldt-Jakob disease, the first stage might most likely take a few months or about a year to complete. However, it is not impossible to detect the dementia status of your loved one at this early stage of their condition.

Have you ever heard of a PET scan? A **PET scan** is a Positron Emission Tomography Scan (Bhargava, 2020). It is a special type of imaging that allows medical experts to see what is going on in a specific body part and how the cells work in that area. A PET scan is more effective than other imaging studies like CT scans, X-rays, or MRIs, as it helps doctors identify important clues or body changes that show the development of a discreet progressive disease like dementia (Bhargava, 2020). Thus, if a PET scan gets conducted on your loved one within the earliest stage of their condition, there is a high possibility that it will help provide an accurate and early diagnosis. Both young and older adults with a family history of certain dementia types with high genetic risk factors can also take advantage of the PET scan to get early verification and know if they have also developed the same condition.

## STAGE 2: AGE-ASSOCIATED MEMORY IMPAIRMENT

At this stage, the cognitive damage in the brain has gotten elevated to some significant extent. Hence, dementia patients begin to showcase subtle signs of their conditions. These symptoms are usually related only to memory deterioration. For example, they could become more forgetful or misplace their belongings. Notwithstanding, these symptoms tend to make little to no impact or changes on the behavior and lifestyle of the affected person. They still perform their daily tasks independently. And on occasions where your loved one even forgets people's names, the location of their things, or details of previous conversations, they always end up remembering. In fact, recent research studies have revealed that people experiencing stage 2 dementia will easily ace the memory test during their clinical examination with a healthcare expert (Gupta, 2022). Ultimately, most people are less likely to notice these signs. But even if anyone notices, they, including healthcare providers, often do not understand that such memory deterioration could be a warning sign of developing dementia. Instead, they may associate these symptoms with aging. And based on what we learned while exploring the differences between the symptoms of normal aging and dementia in Chapter 1, you will also agree that nobody is wrong to make such an association.

Do you recall we said that the major difference between age-related memory impairment and dementia memory loss is that the symptoms of the former do not interfere with the affected person's ability to live independently? Thus, it is right to conclude that the symptoms exhibited by dementia patients at this second stage are specific signs of age-related memory impairment, as it does not cause any significant negative impact on their lives.

## STAGE 3: MILD COGNITIVE IMPAIRMENT

At this stage, most family members and close friends finally begin to suspect that a person is suffering from something other than the typical side effects of aging. As a caregiver, you will notice significant changes that show a slight deterioration in your loved one's thinking and reasoning abilities.

For example, they tend to have difficulty focusing on tasks and may struggle to complete challenging assignments, especially in the workplace. Their attention spans can become severely impaired over time. As such, you might even start receiving complaints about their poor performance or efficiency at a job where they used to be very productive. But still, within the third stage, let's remember that there are already existing symptoms of memory impairment in the picture. However, at stage 3, we can hardly describe the memory impairment of a dementia patient as 'age-related.' It gets slightly worse than the normal memory problems associated with aging. So, for instance, you might notice that their forgetfulness becomes more frequent than usual.

Memory impairment at this stage is still categorized within the minor range (Hallstrom, 2022). So, you might observe that your loved one keeps forgetting about scheduled appointments or recent details that have just been said to him or her. They also tend to misplace their belongings and things of value without remembering the location for a long time. Because of this constant forgetfulness, they ask numerous questions about the same issue.

Despite the mild cognitive impairment and memory problems, dementia patients might still be able to live and perform their daily tasks independently at stage 3. However, it is very important that you get an accurate diagnosis of the exact dementia type affecting your loved one. With that early diagnosis, you can help them begin their treatment process as soon as possible. A diary to record the noticeable behavioral changes your loved one exhibits daily is also a great idea. You can even convince your loved one to reduce stress by retiring from their job and focusing on activities that improve their memory and cognitive abilities.

According to research studies, the third stage of dementia mostly lasts 2 to 5 years, depending on the type of dementia involved (Gupta, 2022). However, the same studies have shown that it is possible to prolong those years and keep stage 3 dementia symptoms as mild as possible. As a caregiver, the best way you take advantage of such an incredible opportunity is to ensure that your dementia loved one gets diagnosed early and receives adequate medical treatment and personal care during the first two to five years of stage 3.

## STAGE 4: MILD DEMENTIA

While stages 1 to 3 are classified as the *pre-dementia* stage, stages 4 and 5 represent mid-stage dementia. The memory and cognitive impairment symptoms at this stage become worse and more definitive than in stage 3. So, apart from just forgetting people's names and details of recent conversations, your loved one, at the stage of mild dementia, would also be unable to remember certain personal details about themselves. Sometimes they struggle to complete tasks that involve multiple steps, like paying bills, using the phone, cooking, vacuuming, or even driving. They also feel slightly disoriented about time and place, and may take a long time to process and respond whenever somebody says something to them. Sometimes, their responses might even be unrelated to the subject of discussion.

When comparing the severity of these symptoms to those which can be seen in stages 1 through 3, stage 4 indicates that your loved one with dementia is beginning to lose his/her capacity to manage independent living (Gupta, 2022). Thus, it is the best time for you to start offering the ultimate life support. For example, you would help them with household chores and intensive activities like driving. It is important to note that if your family member or friend is already experiencing the symptoms of stage 4 dementia, they should be banned from driving for their safety.

You also must attend to their financial responsibilities and ensure that nobody takes advantage of their cognitive impairment to financially fraud them. You can also keep records of their disease's progression in your diary. This constant recording will help you as a caregiver to trace your dementia loved one's triggers and to understand them better. Nevertheless, medical experts have revealed that it is much easier to diagnose any dementia at this stage because the symptoms are becoming more definitive and obvious. Thus, an elaborate PET scan might not be necessary for accurate diagnosis because a simple Mini-Mental State Examination can easily reveal if a person has dementia and the specific type that the patient has. However, it is of the utmost importance for us as caregivers and family members to be cognizant of our relationships with those suffering from dementia.

This extra caution becomes necessary because, at stage 4, many dementia sufferers often struggle to hide their distress and pain from their loved ones. Thus, we must be vigilant, caring, and gentle in helping them.

## STAGE 5: MODERATE DEMENTIA

At this mid-stage, people living with dementia require a higher degree of assistance and care than what was administered to them in stage 4 (Hallstrom, 2022). Although dementia patients may be able to meet some basic needs like eating, drinking, using the restroom, or bathing independently; unfortunately, at this stage in their life, most have lost a significant amount of cognitive functioning capabilities. Of course, memory loss and cognitive impairment get worse than it was in stage 4. In addition to forgetting personal details about themselves, people living with stage 5 dementia also begin to gradually forget their personal history and the names and faces of their family members and friends. However, the forgetfulness, in this case, is still minor, as they always end up recognizing the closest people to them.

They also develop more complicated symptoms that center on time and place disorientation. So, for example, you will observe that dementia loved ones cannot make sense of what place they are currently at or what time, day, and season it is presently. This time disorientation causes them to be frustrated and confused when choosing their day's outfit. Without help, your loved one could choose summer outfits during heavy snow and cold seasons. Additionally, stage 5 dementia patients also tend to get lost on their way to places that were formerly familiar to them. So, what kind of help and assistance can you provide for your beloved one at this stage?

The most important support step is to ensure that they are getting the right treatment to slow the cognitive decline ongoing in their brain. However, regarding their personal self-care, you need to find effective solutions to help your beloved select appropriate clothing without making them lose their sense of independence. So instead of offering to help while they are raiding through their wardrobe in confusion and frustration, you can select and lay out the outfit before they even wake up in the morning.

Furthermore, you can help to improve your loved one's declining memory by encouraging them to ask questions or tell stories. Clinical studies have shown that it is quite hard for dementia patients to remember details – personal or not – when confronted or asked directly. However, they have sharp imaginations with which they tell stories. As you listen to some of these stories, you will realize that your loved one is still aware of certain facts about themselves and their history. When they forget people's names or details of a recent conversation, you must always remind them in an even and reassuring tone. Doing so helps your loved one to feel more accepted, less judged, and less frustrated.

## STAGE 6: MODERATELY SEVERE DEMENTIA

When the condition of your loved one develops to this later stage of dementia, they exhibit severe symptoms that demand constant supervision, assistance, and care (Gardner, 2021).

In stage 5, we said that dementia patients can still care for their personal needs, like eating and going to the toilet. However, at this stage, they completely lose their ability to perform any task independently. As such, they depend on your help to nourish them, get them dressed, and even move from one place to another. Suppose your loved one is experiencing either Lewy Body Dementia or Parkinson's disease. In that case, they suffer intense muscle stiffness and balance and coordination problems during the sixth stage of their condition.

Apart from the worsening state of their memory and cognitive impairment, stage 6 dementia patients also experience drastic personality and emotional changes. For example, they exhibit hallucination and delusional behaviors like claiming to see or smell things that are not present in their environment, pretending to speak to people when they are alone, preparing to go to work when they have actually retired from their jobs or being paranoid that their caregiver is trying to do something harmful to them.

Your loved one will find it very difficult to recognize your face or remember your name as their primary caregiver, spouse, or child. As such, you might see them getting easily anxious and agitated when you or other family members get close to them. In reaction, they often display violent and aggressive behaviors to resist any help. But, no matter how hostile your loved ones might become due to their condition, there are several effective strategies that you can still take advantage of to offer the best kind of help to them. Again, getting your loved ones enough medical care is the most important help you can offer. Regular checkups are even more crucial at this stage because their immune system weakens.

Studies have shown that a significant percentage of dementia patients do not survive stage 6 because of their fragile immune system which renders them vulnerable to potentially fatal infections like pneumonia (Alzheimer's Society, 2022). According to medical experts, this stage tends to last for an average of one to two years (Ivy Palmer Live-in-Care, 2021). Nevertheless, you can also try to bond with your loved ones by reading to them, engaging in activities they find fun, or even looking over old photos with them. Also, you need to master the art of calmness and patience. Your cool demeanor can help stabilize them emotionally if you can remain calm whenever your loved one throws violent tantrums or has a meltdown.

## STAGE 7: SEVERE DEMENTIA

This final stage is undoubtedly the most critical point of a person's dementia condition. Your loved one loses any little control they might have over their brain and body parts in stage 7. They are no longer aware of their surroundings or what is happening to them. Thus, it becomes the responsibility of their primary caregiver to think on their behalf. This reasoning could be in terms of when and what they get to eat and drink or have to go to the toilet. Ideally, soft and easy-to-swallow foods are the only types of meals that people living with stage 7 dementia can consume.

Their motor skills and speaking ability also suffer severe losses. And the least they can do is utter incoherent sounds or words. They need help to sit up and even open their mouths to get fed. And their meltdown moments also become more frequent and severe. Based on the severity of the symptoms we just highlighted, you would agree that any person living with stage seven dementia would require a kind of supervision and care that is not just around-the-clock but also very professional. Hence, no matter how much you want to take care of your loved one at home, the best decision at this stage is to get professional support which could come in different forms (Gardner, 2021).

The whole family could move the patient to a nursing home that can offer 24-hour quality professional care. However, if you want your loved one to receive the same round-the-clock professional care within the comfort of your home, you can hire a live-in carer or private nurse. This option allows you to be more involved in the care of your loved one. Nevertheless, either of the two options is fine as long as the patient gets all the professional care they need.

And there we have it — the seven critical stages through which every type of dementia progresses. Evidently, having a clear perception of the seven stages of dementia significantly influences your recognition and understanding of your beloved's condition as well as how you approach being their caregiver. We must also note that it takes a lot of observation and attention to truly notice when your loved one transcends from one stage to another. Thus, constantly recording details of your loved ones' behavioral changes in a diary is the easiest and quickest way to notice any shift in their dementia stages.

# AVAILABLE TREATMENTS FOR DEMENTIA

"If you want others to be happy, practice compassion. If you want to be happy, practice compassion."

– Dalai Lama

*Y*ou are aware that there is currently no cure for dementia. However, the good news is that researchers have developed several treatment alternatives to improve the quality of your loved one's life, even in the face of a critical illness like dementia. These treatment alternatives have been clinically tested and proven to be very effective in slowing the progression of cognitive decline, memory loss, and other symptoms associated with dementia.

However, before examining these effective treatment alternatives, you must understand that the first and most critical step in this treatment journey involves getting an accurate diagnosis of your loved one's dementia type from a healthcare expert.

Most caregivers often underestimate the value of diagnosis and jump into getting treatments for their loved ones. However, medical experts have maintained that such negligence could greatly harm the affected patients and further lead to a quicker deterioration of their mental and physical health. Thus, before you even start thinking of treatment options for your loved one, it would be best to first find out the exact type of dementia affecting them. No matter how observant and critical you might be, it is almost impossible for you to single-handedly make an accurate diagnosis. In fact, studies have shown that a single test cannot give an accurate dementia diagnosis (Mayo Clinic, 2021).

Medical experts conduct different examinations, including brain scans, laboratory tests, and neurological and psychiatric evaluations, to come up with a diagnosis. To a large extent, the success of any treatment journey begins with an early professional diagnosis.

Now that we have understood the importance of diagnosis before the commencement of any dementia treatment, the next question to explore is: What are these effective treatment alternatives for dementia? Researchers have developed three major treatment categories for managing dementia symptoms. They include medications, therapies, and lifestyle remedies. So, without stalling any further, let's analyze each category.

## MEDICATIONS FOR DEMENTIA

After countless research and clinical examinations in the last few decades, researchers have successfully developed certain medications to help slow and manage the various memory, physical, cognitive, and emotional problems associated with dementia. Because of the popularity of Alzheimer's disease over other dementia types, most of these drugs got designed specifically for Alzheimer's patients. However, medical experts have confirmed that they sometimes prescribe some of these medications for treating other types of dementia (Mayo Clinic, 2022). The U. S. Food and Drug Administration has approved two major categories of Alzheimer's medications. They include drugs that are designed to delay the progression of dementia and drugs that help in temporarily mitigating cognitive dementia symptoms like memory loss, reasoning, and thinking problems.

## ALZHEIMER'S DRUGS THAT SLOW DISEASE PROGRESSION

- **Aducanumab (Aduhelm)**

This drug is the most recently approved medication for Alzheimer's disease. But we must take a few steps backward to understand how it works. You would remember that while discussing the development of Alzheimer's in Chapter 2, we mentioned that its main cause is a toxic protein called Amyloid beta, which gets built up to abnormal levels in the brain and ends up killing its cells. These brain cells' death can lead to a gradual deterioration in cognitive functioning and the inability to remember things (memory loss). However, when the Aducanumab medication gets introduced into your loved one's body, it targets and stops the progressive build-up of these amyloid plaques. Similarly, it gradually reduces their abnormal levels. By doing so, the medication slowly allows for restoring the communication between the brain nerve cells that the amyloid plaques disrupted (Melinosky, 2022).

To properly perform the functions we just highlighted, Aducanumab often causes swelling and bleeding in certain brain areas, thus creating several side effects in dementia patients. Some of such effects include headaches, nausea, vision challenges, dizziness, or confusion (Alzheimer's Association, 2021).

## ALZHEIMER'S DRUGS THAT MITIGATE COGNITIVE DEMENTIA SYMPTOMS

- **Cholinesterase Inhibitors**

These inhibitors work by preventing the breakdown or decline of a particular chemical messenger called *Acetylcholine* (Mayo

Clinic, 2021). This chemical messenger is essential for maintaining one's emotional balance (personal mood), as well as sustaining their ability to remember (memory) and learn (learning skills), qualities that are severely affected by dementia progression. Thus, by preventing its breakdown of acetylcholine, cholinesterase inhibitors delay the worsening of several dementia symptoms related to memory, emotions, and learning.

Currently, the U. S. Food and Drug Administration (FDA) has approved only three major medications as cholinesterase inhibitors like *Donepezil* (Aricept), *Rivastigmine* (Exelon), and *Galantamine* (Razadyne). Although cholinesterase inhibitors usually get administered to people living with stage 2 to 5 Alzheimer's disease, it is not completely tolerable. Sometimes, they result in unpleasant side effects. Some side effects are decreased or loss of appetite, regurgitation (nausea) and vomiting, and increased bowel movements (Alzheimer's Association, 2021).

- **Glutamate Regulators (Memantine)**

Like cholinesterase inhibitors, glutamate regulators also target a chemical compound in the brain called *glutamate*. Glutamate is a neurotransmitter (messenger) that plays crucial roles in regulating different brain processes, including memory, language, judgment, and reasoning (Alzheimer's Association, 2021). Thus, by regulating the activity of this important chemical messenger, glutamate regulators enable your brain to begin to process information appropriately and gradually. This effect, in turn, prevents worsening symptoms related to the brain processes regulated by glutamate.

Research studies have revealed that *Memantine*, the major drug under this category, offers effective treatment results to patients with stage 2 to 6 dementia. However, this treatment often comes at the cost of various side effects like nausea, migraine-like headaches, constipation, and dizziness.

## THERAPIES FOR DEMENTIA

Despite the effective impacts that the medications we just analyzed could have on the well-being of your dementia loved one, we cannot ignore how critical some of their side effects might be. In some cases, the severity of a patient's condition may even hinder them from using these medications. Hence, medical experts often recommend that dementia patients get treated first using non-drug strategies like therapies and life-style remedies (Weill Institute for Neuroscience, 2021). Though these treatment methods might not be as effective as the medications, they cause little to no side effects on the mental and physical state of your loved ones. Here are some of the most effective therapy types recommended for dementia patients.

- **Cognitive Stimulation Therapy (CST)**

According to the National Institute for Clinical Excellence, the CST type is the most effective non-drug treatment for dementia (Lifted Team, 2021). CST is a *structured* therapy program that majorly helps patients in stages 2 through 5.

**So how does it work?**

When your loved one begins cognitive stimulation therapy, they are introduced to a group of five to eight other dementia patients. The group meets at least 14 times and engages in discussions and activities drawn from a specific predetermined theme: food, money, childhood, or politics. But the group members need help from a facilitator to have these discussions and activities. So, there is always a well-trained professional who leads the discussions and activities and helps in creating a supportive and friendly atmosphere for everyone.

The discussions and activities are designed to be fun for the participants while simultaneously helping them improve their cognitive abilities, memory, and language skills. So, for example, if this week's theme centers on food, the participants might have to share details about their favorite meals and why they love them, etc. The entire group could also play games or songs centered on food. In most cases, CST sessions take place in aging and memory centers or nursing homes. But it could also take place in a one-to-one setting.

- **Reality Orientation Therapy (ROT)**

Like CST, Reality Orientation Therapy can be especially effective for individuals with dementia in stages 2 through 5 as well.
It involves a *conversion-based* approach where your loved one
gets presented with factual information about their personal
history, dates, places, recent events, or even people's names
and relationships with those people.

You may wonder if these details get read out to the patients,
word for word. No! The trained therapist smartly incorporates
the information when casually conversing with the patient.
Thus, by using the tool of social interaction to provide
dementia patients with subtle reminders about their current
reality, this therapy aims to gently and gradually draw them
out of their disoriented and confused state. Sometimes, as they
internalize the information about their present reality, it challenges their sense of thinking and reasoning. Consequently,
their memories might also get triggered. So, as you can see,
ROT is truly a multi-beneficial therapy. It simultaneously but
gradually tackles common dementia symptoms like memory
deterioration, cognitive decline, time and place disorientation,
and even social interaction problems. Nevertheless, compassion, calmness, and gentility are the core elements that every
reality orientation therapist must exercise to achieve successful
results with their patients. Sometimes your loved one might be
so deeply grounded in their false reality that they will always
disagree with the subtle factual reminders presented during
their therapy sessions. In such cases, it is best to back off from
trying to orient them and instead join them in discussing that
false reality they strongly believe. Using that experience, you

can develop a more compassionate way to incorporate those facts into your causal conversations.

• **Reminiscence Therapy**

Studies have shown that even when people with dementia lose touch with their current reality and self-awareness, they still manage to hold onto their most cherished memories. This fact serves as the basis for reminiscence therapy. It is a non-drug treatment approach that employs different stimulating sensory materials and experiences to help dementia patients recall memories of people, events, and places (Samuels, 2021). This therapy differs from the rest because your loved one does not get directly confronted to remember certain memories. So rather than asking them direct questions like "Can you remember where you grew up? Or, what elementary school did you attend?" The goal of reminiscence therapy is to enable those memories to surface in their minds naturally.

But how is that magical recollection even supposed to happen if they are not pressured? You employ materials like photographs, music, scent, or even food taste to stimulate their senses like sight (vision), smell (olfactory), sound (auditory/hearing), taste (gustatory), or touch (tactile), as the case may be (Eldercare alliance, 2017). With the right stimulation, those hidden memories will surely resurface.

Here is what a typical reminisce therapy session would look like. The therapist engages your loved one in casual conversations to get them comfortable. As they interact, their therapist pulls out some familiar family photos and goes through them with their patients. Though it might not happen at the very first attempt, your loved one's sense of sight gets stimulated and elicits the memories of the people in that photo or the events that led to that photo. Consequently, they might burst into a storytelling mood and begin recounting what happens before, during, and after the photos and the other people in them.

In other cases, sensory stimulation and memory recollection could result from hearing their favorite childhood songs or seeing prized objects from their past. But notwithstanding the type of techniques or sensory materials employed in the recollection process, reminiscence therapy focuses mainly on exploring the positive memories of dementia patients. By recalling their best and most positive memories, your loved one develops positive feelings of happiness and confidence in their abilities (Samuels, 2021). They also preserve their sense of identity despite their illness.

- **Occupational Therapy**

In occupational therapy, your loved one first gets assessed to determine their specific difficulties, needs, potential risk factors, favorite activities, and interests. Using the information gathered from this assessment, the therapist develops an effective plan of new techniques you can adopt to help your loved one improve their memory and cognitive function for as long as possible (Wilson, 2019). These techniques could include communication, memory improvement, or routine planning. An occupational therapist could even recommend that your loved one take up any other therapy types we examined previously.

They also inform and help you source the right equipment that reduces the difficulties encountered by your loved one. For example, suppose the patient is struggling with mobility problems. The therapist can help you source the right comfy chair or wheelchair to reduce muscle stiffness or coordination struggles. Ultimately, an occupational therapist works with caregivers and families of dementia patients to improve the physical and mental well-being of their patients.


## LIFESTYLE REMEDIES FOR DEMENTIA

Getting diagnosed with dementia is a life-changing event for anyone, whether young or old. Hence, in addition to the medications and therapies adopted to manage its symptoms effectively, dementia caregivers are also expected to introduce crucial adjustments to their loved ones' lifestyles. Recent clinical studies have revealed that these lifestyle readjustments significantly enhance the effectiveness of medications and therapies, no matter how small they seem. So, as a caregiver, here are some lifestyle remedies that you can adopt to improve the mental and physical well-being of your loved one.

- **Routine Planning**

Creating a stable routine plan for your loved ones right from the early stages of their diagnosis is an incredible lifestyle remedy that becomes even more significant later. Daily routines enable people with dementia to navigate their lives with a better sense of order (American Seniors Housing Association, 2021). The more consistent they become at practicing these routines, the better they will be at predicting how they should spend every hour of their days. Hence, even when they lose their time and day orientation or their ability to do everyday tasks, they are still aware of the order in which their daily activities follow. Such stability gives them a sense of independence and makes them less frustrated and agitated. Ultimately, when your loved one remains less agitated, it makes your job as a caregiver easier.

- **Proper Diet**

Consuming balanced varieties of healthy foods and drinks is necessary for every dementia patient. Their nutrition is just as important as their medications and therapies. Proper nutrition helps in managing weight loss symptoms. It also improves the patients' muscular strength and makes the bones less susceptible to mobility problems.

The healthy foods expected in an ideal diet for dementia patients include lean protein, vegetables, whole grains, fruits, and low-fat dairy products (Alzheimer's Association, 2021). It is also important to cut out specific food with high refined sugar, sodium (salt), and saturated fats from your loved one's diet to achieve effective results. Notwithstanding the powerful benefits of proper nutrition, we cannot ignore that, as your loved one's condition progresses, there are likely to be significant changes in their food preferences and appetite. Thus, you have to be flexible with their meal choices. Eating together with them might also help in improving their appetite. Sometimes, it could take them up to an hour to finish up. In such cases, you have to be patient with them. During the later dementia stages, where your loved one loses control over their brain and body, it is important to ensure they get their food at the right time and at the normal temperature.

- **Light Exercising**

In Chapter 1, we mentioned exercising as an effective way of lowering the risk of dementia development in older adults. However, it is also useful in lessening the severe symptoms in dementia patients. Although older patients might not be able to perform high-intensity workouts, they can still take advantage of some moderate or low-intensity exercises. It could be as simple as stretching and seated balance moves or more intense aerobics like walking, cycling, swimming, or even dancing.

Medical research has proven that these physical activities are quite effective in improving certain symptoms of dementia, like muscle stiffness, balance, and coordination problems. Beyond physicality, these studies have also shown that exercising could be very helpful in improving the emotional and cognitive functioning of people with dementia. It particularly helps in making them less restless and agitated.

On that positive note, we'll close this chapter. However, you must understand that every medication, therapy, or lifestyle remedy discussed in this chapter does not count as medical advice but as information to help you get more enlightened about your loved one's condition. As such, a qualified health-care provider should always be your only medical advice and recommendation source. With their guidance, you will surely find the best and most effective medications and non-drug treatments for improving the quality of your loved one's life, even with their dementia condition.

# UNDERSTANDING THE PATIENT'S PERSPECTIVE

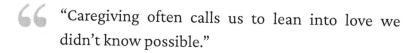

"Caregiving often calls us to lean into love we didn't know possible."

– Tia Walker

$\mathcal{U}$ntil now, we have only examined the dynamics of dementia from a more general perspective — the researchers' findings or the medical experts' explanations. However, the most important fact we, as caregivers, need to understand is that every patient experiences dementia differently. We must also consider our loved one's perspective on experiencing dementia as well. Gaining such knowledge, specifically from their point of view, is more effective in helping you provide the right and best kind of care.

## PERSONALITY CHANGES

In the previous chapters, we explained that personality and behavioral changes are major symptoms common to all types of dementia. For some dementia types, these changes occur at the initial stages, but for others, it could be a more sudden transformation that happens much later. Notwithstanding, when your loved one begins to act out of their usual character, the truth remains that these personality changes do not just develop out of the blue. Certain factors lead to such development. But before examining those factors, let's first understand the connection between personality and behaviors and how it relates to dementia. As humans, our personalities reflect the embodiment of who we are, from our beliefs and values to our personal traits and emotional characteristics. However, our behaviors, which are how we act on the outside, spring from our inherent personalities. So let's use an example to illustrate how this connection works.

For as long as you can remember, your mother has always had a gentle personality. As such, she always talks in a cool tone and never raises her voice at anyone. It's likely you've observed how her character shapes her behavior. Nevertheless, when dementia sets in, it forces a significant change in how its victims see themselves, their pattern of thoughts, and their emotional feelings. What happens on the inside is always reflected on the outside. Exactly! Thus, because of the changes in their inherent personality, people with dementia begin to do things and act in ways that are quite different from their "old selves." Let's find out what factors and conditions contribute to personality changes in dementia patients.

## WHY DO DEMENTIA PATIENTS BECOME DIFFERENT FROM THEIR OLD SELVES?

- **Fear**

Being able to age gracefully in good health and surrounded by family is a commonly shared desire among people. However, just one moment of dementia diagnosis sends that dream crashing down. Fear is usually the first reaction of older adults after their dementia diagnosis. Because they have seen, heard, or read about how dementia transforms people's lives for the worse, they cannot help but become scared of what the future holds for them, and negative thoughts easily infiltrate their minds.

Most people are unaware of how complex and powerful fear can be, but this single emotion can negatively transform your loved one's thinking process. It steals their inner peace, and the chaos that they are internally feeling could cause them to act differently and completely out of character. So, fear could lead your mother, who had always had a gentle personality and had never raised her voice to anyone, to suddenly begin to yell and even curse at people.

- **Pain**

Most people assume that because dementia mainly affects the brain, it cannot cause physical pain. However, constipation, muscular problems, and urinary tract infections are common physical conditions that dementia patients encounter (Weill Institute for Neurosciences, 2021). But no matter how much we know and love our relatives and friends who get diagnosed with dementia, we'll never be able to understand the physical and mental pains that they experience on a daily basis.

In the early stages, they might still be able to communicate how they feel. However, they lose that ability as their condition progress. Consequently, the fact that your loved one can neither share their pain nor get anyone to understand them could make them angry, easily irritated, violent, or lonely.

- **Frustration Over the Loss of Independence and Self-Control**

Humans are naturally egoistic beings who love to take charge of their lives. However, being diagnosed with dementia automatically deprives your loved one of their independence and self-control. Since they have lived most of their life without relying on anyone, seeing other people take over their life infuriates them. To a large extent, the fact that they need to seek someone's help to do even the most things that are making them feel weak and incapable. That loss of independence and self-control also affects their self-esteem negatively. As such, they get to a point where it becomes very frustrating and painful. Thus, they try to regain independence by resisting any help, no matter how badly they need it. In most cases, they resort to violence and aggressiveness to resist what they consider the taking over of their life.

- **Environment**

Many dementia patients become highly sensitive to environmental factors as their condition progresses. This hypersensitivity could be in terms of sound, light, smell, or texture. You might notice that your loved one begins to complain or react negatively in an environment that used to be their favorite. For example, your husband might have loved reading on the balcony of your house, which is quite close to the main road. However, his dementia made him hypersensitive to loud sounds.

That new development will automatically make him react negatively in his former favorite spot, and any attempt to make him go out there even for fresh air could end badly. Such a person is likely to behave differently in a room with different people making noise or where there is loud music or sound from a TV set.

- **Mental Conditions**

In the previous chapters, we mentioned how dementia patients experience delusions and hallucinations, especially at the mid and later stages of their condition. These two conditions contribute greatly to the personality and behavioral changes experienced by people living with dementia. Because they constantly believe, see, smell, taste, or hear things that are not present or real, your dementia loved one finds themselves in a different reality from yours. This change in reality also leads to a corresponding change in their personality and behaviors. While trapped in their delusional reality, the patient gets easily confused and frightened because they see everyone, including you, the primary care-giver, as a threat to them. Hence, when people come close or attempt to help them, they react differently and negatively in most cases.

Apart from delusions and hallucinations, dementia patients also experience severe symptoms of depression and anxiety. This mental illness also tends to have powerful effects on their personalities and behaviors. They may become aggressive, and irritable, and have difficulty controlling their emotions. They may also experience confusion and disorientation.

- **Medications**

You will remember that in the last chapter, we examined several approved medications for dementia, each of which had its side effects. Some of them include mental confusion, headaches, dizziness, and drowsiness. Such effects can change your loved one's personality and behaviors, dampening their spirits and putting them in greater pain. As a way of coping with those discomforts, some patients become restless or take an obsessive interest in something that can keep them distracted. It could even make them more sexually active than they were before their diagnosis.

## BEHAVIORAL CHANGES IN DEMENTIA PATIENTS

Now that we have understood the factors and conditions causing our loved ones to act differently after their diagnosis, our next task is to break down some of the most common behavioral changes that dementia patients tend to showcase. Unfortunately, most caregivers in the dementia community tend to believe that these behaviors are only challenging to them. However, as we analyze these behavioral changes from the patient's perspective, we'll understand that your loved ones are not simply trying to act difficult. Rather, those behaviors are equally challenging to them as they are to you.

## REPETITIVE BEHAVIORS

As their condition progresses, most dementia patients begin to say and do things repeatedly, and it often seems like they have lost control. These repetitive behaviors could include asking the same question repeatedly, mumbling the same word or phrase repeatedly, constantly checking their wallet or purse, fidgeting, zipping and unzipping their cardigans, and flapping their hands or rocking their body.

Sometimes, you cannot help but think that your loved one is deliberately annoying, but they are not. In most cases, their memory deterioration makes it impossible to remember that they have said or done something before. Because nothing truly gets stored in their short-term memory, your loved one might be unaware that they are saying the same phrase, repeating the same action, or asking the same questions.

In other cases, dementia patients might exhibit repetitive behaviors because they feel anxious or confused about something. Thus, the repetitive behaviors you find annoying might be a major source of calmness and comfort for your loved one.

## COMBATIVENESS

Combativeness, in this context, refers to the intense physical aggression often exhibited by dementia patients. For example, the combative behaviors of a typical dementia patient could include biting, grabbing people's hair, kicking, pushing, or spitting at others (Heerem, 2021). The behaviors mostly get triggered when you or other relatives try to offer care or help to your loved one.

Again, remember that they are not trying to be hotheaded or difficult. On the contrary, they probably don't recognize or remember you. So, instead of seeing your gesture as a form of support, they consider it an intrusion into their personal space or a threat to harm them. At first, they often try to resist with just their words. However, when the "stranger" does not listen and keeps nagging them to eat, shower, or get dressed, as the case may be, they resort to their last option: physical aggression.

94

## EXAGGERATED OUTBURSTS AND REACTIONS

Apart from using physical aggression to combat and resist offers of assistance from people, dementia patients also experience intense episodes of anger and violence. These outbursts could be yelling, verbally abusing people, throwing and breaking things, attempting to attack others physically, or inflicting harm on themselves.

The truth is that no human is above experiencing certain moments of anger and aggression. However, dementia exaggerates those emotions even when the patients have never had any anger issues. While a dementia patient's combativeness often gets triggered by the offer of care, the causes of their exaggerated anger outbursts are tied to three major factors that we have already examined in the previous chapters. They include physical pain, fear, and environmental factors. Thus, when you see your loved one reacting to little things with exaggerated anger, the reaction might not be linked to that particular incident. Rather, it could be because of their pent-up fear or inability to share and get rid of the pain they feel in different parts of their body.

## LOSS OF PERSONAL INHIBITIONS

Due to their progressive cognitive decline, people with dementia often experience drastic changes in their inhibitions. Their condition makes them lose their sense of self-consciousness, and they tend to behave contrary to the usual rules of social interaction (Dementia Australia, 2020). So you might see your usually polite loved one transform into a rude person who always makes hurtful comments at you, other family members, or even random strangers in public. They could also display impulsive behaviors like undressing in public or highly inappropriate sexual behaviors like flirting openly and touching their genitals in public spaces. Of course, it is normal for you as a caregiver to feel shocked, embarrassed, and frustrated when your loved one display such dis-inhibited behaviors in public. However, remember that your loved one is not intentionally trying to be inappropriate. In fact, they might even believe they are behaving the right way. The inappropriate behaviors could also result from their feeling of discomfort. For example, they might only take off their clothes in public because they feel uncomfortable.

## COGNITIVE & MOTOR CHANGES

Apart from their personalities and behaviors, dementia patients experience many negative changes and decline in their cognitive and motor functioning abilities. Let's examine some of the major cognitive problems your loved one will probably experience as their condition progresses.

- **Memory Changes**

It is no secret that memory deterioration is a hallmark symptom of any form of dementia. However, you must understand that these memory changes are different for every patient. For some people, their condition deprives them of the ability to create new memories (Alzheimer's Association, 2021). As a result, the things they see, do, and hear are not recorded in their short-term or long-term memory. Since nothing gets recorded in their memory, it becomes impossible to recall what a person says or what happened in a recent event, even when they were present and heard what the other person had said. Other dementia patients, however, get the chance to create and store new memories in the brain and mind, but their condition makes it difficult to retrieve such information when the need arises, or it completely denies access to those stored information and memories. Notwithstanding how these memory changes occur, there is no denying that it limits the abilities of its victims in so many ways. For example, they find it almost impossible to concentrate on anything because their poor memory makes them lose track of important details, times, dates, or even the faces of their loved ones.

Although your loved ones' memory changes can create significant challenges for you, they also hate that they cannot remember even the simplest things. To a large extent, their memory loss diminishes their self-esteem and makes them feel like they have lost some essential part of themselves.

- **Speech and Communication Problems**

Communication is undoubtedly an important aspect of every human's life. It is the perfect medium through which we convey our needs, emotions, and feelings to the right people who can help us take care of them. But what happens when one cannot express those important elements properly? It's extremely frustrating! That emotion sums up the reality of many people with dementia. As their condition progresses through the mid and later stages, they lose the greater part of their speaking and reasoning ability; these two skills go hand in hand. Thus, by losing both, it becomes even harder for your loved one to communicate their needs and feelings with you or other family members. So, even in pain or extreme discomfort, they often sit in silence and endure. Then, when it reaches a point when they can no longer cope with it, they resort to acting aggressively to gain the attention of their caregivers.

- **Loss of Motor Coordination**

One of the major factors that cause dementia patients to lose their independence is the loss of their fine motor skills. These skills enable humans to complete basic tasks like bathing, dressing, eating breakfast, opening and closing the door, etc. However, when dementia begins to progress through a person's brain, it disrupts the connection and communication between the brain cells and the spinal cord, thus leading to the loss of motor coordination around the body (Bennett and Buchman, 2012). By losing motor coordination, your loved one suffers both physical and mental pains — the results of the physical pain from problems like muscle stiffness and rigidity. However, the mental and emotional pain is tied to the patient's gradual loss of independence that they have enjoyed for most of their life. Fear then sets in when they realize symptoms could get worse in the next few years, and they may not be able to move any part of their body.

- **Blurred Vision Problems**

Almost every older adult seeks reading glasses as they advance through their 40s and 50s — the effect of the natural aging process on our eyesight fuels this general action. However, the vision problem is more critical with dementia, as its patients experience severe visual difficulties while still having healthy eyes.

This ironic development occurs because the visual problem results from the ongoing cognitive decline in the brain and not because of an eye infection. So, your loved ones might be able to see but have difficulty making the right sense of what they see. As a result, they experience symptoms like not recognizing the face of someone they can see, misjudging the distance between staircases, and mistaking random reflections or shadows for concrete objects.

Some researchers have discovered that cognitive vision problem is the primary cause of the visual hallucinations often experienced by most dementia patients; the blurriness in their eyesight causes them to see things that are not even present in that environment.

## INDEPENDENT OR ASSISTED LIVING

Based on what we have discussed so far, it is safe to conclude that we have all gotten a clear understanding of the different dementia-based problems from the perspective of our loved one. In addition, we have seen firsthand how dementia transforms them into a completely different person with diverse physical, mental, and emotional pains.

Your compassion for your dementia loved one might have skyrocketed, higher than before you picked up this book. And perhaps, the biggest dilemma in your mind right now is how you can help to make your loved one's life as normal and painless as possible. Typically, your first concern will most likely center on their living condition. But, of course, you probably had your own life before your loved one got diagnosed with dementia. So what happens now? Do you pause your life to deliver your caregiver roles effectively?

As much as that option seems the best, it might not be feasible for you and your loved one. To start with, you would remember we said earlier in this chapter that most dementia patients hate to lose their independence to someone else. They would rather take control of themselves for as long as their dementia conditions allow them because doing so will likely make them feel more self-confident, happy, and fulfilled. And living alone is the best way they can enjoy such independence. Does that sound like a bad idea? Let's find out if it is truly possible and safe for your loved one to live alone after being diagnosed with dementia.

## CAN YOUR LOVED ONE LIVE ALONE WITH DEMENTIA?

First, it might surprise you that one-third of dementia patients in the U. S. live alone. However, these statistics do not imply that every dementia patient can safely live an independent lifestyle. Instead, it tells us that the possibility of independent living truly exists for your loved one. But it is dependable on the stage of their dementia and the fulfillment of safety precautions in their homes. So let's analyze each of these two factors.

Based on the level of disease progression, dementia patients in their initial stages of dementia have a high chance of living independently without any problems. In Chapter 3, you will remember that we discussed the seven main stages of dementia, with stages 1, 2, and 3 being the initial stages of dementia. For example, suppose your loved one is only showing the symptoms of cognitive impairment (stage 1), age-loss memory impairment (stage 2), and mild cognitive impairment (stage 3). In that case, they are among the patients in a better position to navigate their daily life with little to no help. Notwithstanding, being at the initial stages of dementia does not stop your loved ones from being at a high risk of falls, malnutrition, wandering due to confusion and memory deterioration, and loneliness. To a large extent, each of these conditions could be life-threatening. However, because your dementia patient already has a lower level of disease progression, it is possible to lower these risk factors using certain effective strategies (National Institute on Aging, 2021).

As a caregiver, here are tips you can take advantage of to ensure the safety of your loved one if they are determined to stay alone during the early stages of their dementia.

- Start by scanning and setting their home for safety. For example, it would help if you got rid of throw rugs, electrical cords lying on the floor, or any other unsafe items that can make them more susceptible to falls. You can also install safety devices like emergency call buttons, fall monitors, and smoke and carbon monoxide detectors.

- Visit them daily or at least weekly to interact with them and make them feel less lonely. You can also help them with cleaning, cooking, or other household chores during your visitation. First, however, you must ensure that you don't make them incapable of doing their tasks alone.

- Join them in planning and organizing their daily activities. You can help them in creating to-do lists and set important reminders on the calendar, especially in terms of their medications. If you don't live close to them, ensure that you share their diagnosis with their closest neighbors. These people are likely to be the first to notice if your loved one goes wandering or does not come home. By informing them and sharing your contacts with them, they can always reach out to you about your loved one when the need arises.

- Encourage them to get connected with technological devices like smartphones and tablets. These devices can remain connected with you and other family members through video calls or social media messages. These gadgets can also serve as the perfect alarm and plan organizers.

Of course, there is no doubt that these tips will surely help make your loved one's independent life as safe and easy as possible. However, we cannot ignore what lies ahead in the future. You remember dementia is a progressive illness. Thus, within only a few months of living alone, your loved one's condition might have progressed to a stage in which they can no longer drive or properly take care of their financials. So what do you do when that time comes? Let's find out!

## CAN YOUR LOVED ONE STILL DRIVE WITH DEMENTIA?

We all know that driving is a complex task that requires high concentration and quick reaction on the part of the person taking control of the vehicle. Unfortunately, a dementia patient will not be able to fulfill those requirements when their condition progresses to some point, usually the fourth dementia stage. At that point, they gradually begin to showcase different noticeable signs. Some of these include forgetting the location or route to the destination they are driving to, ignoring traffic signs, driving beyond the speed limits, losing lane control, and hitting curbs outside (Alzheimer's Association, 2021).

Immediately after your loved one begins to exhibit these signs of unsafe driving, the best and safest option is to get them to retire from driving and take up other transportation alternatives. These alternatives may include giving their driving responsibilities to other family members, including yourself, or arranging for a reliable and personal taxi service (Alzheimer's Association, 2021). You could also reduce their driving needs by making them adopt more delivery services.

Although these alternatives are the better choice for your dementia loved one, getting them to make that huge move is often easier said than done. There is a high possibility that your loved one will perceive their retirement from driving as another big loss of their independence. Hence, they will do all they can to resist your offer. Nevertheless, you can confront and overcome such huge resistance by having an honest and sympathetic dialogue with them. It would be best to acknowledge that you understand how they feel about the initiative while simultaneously appealing to their sense of responsibility. You can also stress why it is important for them to take that move and reassure them that the available alternatives are just as great as self-driving. However, if these personal one-to-one conversations fail to do the job, you can get their physician or healthcare provider to make the recommendation. Because they hold these experts in high regard, they will most likely get persuaded to retire from driving and choose a suitable alternative from the available ones.

## CAN YOUR LOVED ONE STILL MANAGE THEIR FINANCES WITH DEMENTIA?

Legal and financial planning is an important aspect of every human's life. Unfortunately for people with dementia, when they reach the mid and later stages of the illness, they lose the ability to independently handle their financial and legal responsibilities. Thus, they lie to their primary caregivers or loved ones when they are asked if they paid their bills, prepared their tax returns, claimed their government benefits, or managed their bank accounts. In most cases, they usually don't have a choice in how their finances get managed after their illness progress to a severe point.

As caregivers, however, we can change that pattern by ensuring that our loved ones sort out their legal and financial matters right from the early stages of their dementia diagnosis. They still have a larger part of cognitive functioning intact. Hence, they will be able to make sound decisions concerning their financials. Then, as a family, you can come together to estimate how much your loved one's dementia care will cost in the short term and long term. With that knowledge, you can draft the most effective financial plans to manage the care cost.

## CAN YOUR LOVED ONE STILL WORK AFTER THE DEMENTIA DIAGNOSIS

Medical experts have recommended that dementia patients quit their jobs right after being diagnosed with the illness. They claim that at the point of diagnosis, the disease is already at a highly progressive stage. As such, the external stress from working could increase the rate at which the cognitive decline progresses.

Although most dementia patients would love to slow their cognitive decline by retiring from their jobs after their diagnosis, such actions might have serious consequences for their family, especially when their job is the family's primary source of income. As a result, some dementia patients often take up less stressful jobs to mitigate the likely consequences. Ultimately, deciding to continue or stop working after being diagnosed with dementia is very personal and depends on what your loved one considers to be more beneficial between the two options. Would they rather keep working until the condition develops to a stage where they can no longer cope? Or would they respect the recommendation of medical experts and retire from their jobs as early as possible so they can focus on delaying their cognitive decline? As a caregiver, you are responsible for convincing your dementia loved one to make the right choice. To make things easier, you can use the same approach we analyzed to convince your loved one to retire from driving.

On that note, we have successfully completed the first part of the dementia puzzle, which has to do with *the patient's perspective*. However, completing one part only solves part of that puzzle. Let's now begin to complete the other part by exploring *your perspective as the caregiver.*

# THE CAREGIVER'S PERSPECTIVE AND ROLE

66 "When we honestly ask ourselves which person in our lives means the most to us, we often find that it is those who, instead of giving advice, solutions, or cures, have chosen rather to share our pain and touch our wounds with a warm and tender hand."

– Henri Nouwen

$\mathcal{U}$nderstanding the dynamics of dementia from the perspective of your loved one, who is at the center of it all, is a crucial step in every caregiver's journey. However, it is not enough to enable you to effectively deliver the best care without sacrificing your physical, mental, and emotional well-being. Thus, while delivering unpaid but rewarding caregiving

JANET G. CRUZ

to your loved one, you also need to focus on yourself by addressing how your loved one's dementia diagnosis has transformed the different aspects of your life.

Many caregivers today need a better perception of their caregiving roles. They believe that being a dementia caregiver is only about dedicating their time, money, and energy to the patients. Hence, they always treat their personal needs and issues as insignificant compared to the needs of their loved ones who are going through the actual disease and its painful experiences. To them, doing otherwise will be an act of selfishness. However, the first thing you must understand and accept as a caregiver is that there is nothing selfish about acknowledging and addressing the physical, emotional, and mental toll that your loved one's condition has had on you. On the contrary, such self-care actions are equally beneficial to your dementia loved one as they are to you.

You can only offer your loved one the best and proper support if you are physically, emotionally, and mentally okay. So rather than being selfish, you act out of love and nobility by taking care of yourself while offering the best care and support to your dementia loved one. Hence, in this chapter, our primary goal is to trace the impact of a loved one's dementia diagnosis from the broader perspective, which is the entire family, to the narrow perspective, which involves you, their primary caregiver.

## IMPACT OF A LOVED ONE'S DEMENTIA DIAGNOSIS ON THE ENTIRE FAMILY

According to the Centers for Disease Control, over 90% of dementia patients in the United States experience family caregiving. Of course, no family ever expects it when their loved one receives a dementia diagnosis. The news of that diagnosis will undoubtedly trigger them to experience different emotions, ranging from shock and fear to sadness and frustration. But, more than these emotional problems, having a loved one diagnosed with dementia destabilizes the family's everyday lifestyle. With no prior planning, the whole family suddenly finds themselves at the critical point of dilemma where they must make many crucial decisions concerning the patient.

Some of these decisions usually center on who takes up the primary caregiving role, the patient's living arrangements, and treatment options, and how the family gets the financial resources to settle the cost of care. Conflict erupts among family members during this decision-making process and throughout the healing journey. For example, conflict could arise when some family members refuse to accept the responsibilities designated to them because they lack the ability, resources, or emotional capability to do so. In other cases, it could be because other family members have unrealistic expectations or demands of their primary caregiver.

Apart from creating conflicts within a family, a loved one's dementia condition also creates a massive financial burden on the entire family, especially when there is no adequate savings or health insurance to mitigate the costs. Hence, family members have to cut back on their personal spending to contribute to the payments of direct expenses like diagnostic tests, physician care, and pharmaceuticals (Unicity Healthcare, 2021).

## THE CAREGIVER'S ROLE

Becoming the primary caregiver within the family, either out of necessity or choice, is a full-time commitment that often transforms different aspects of your life. Most times, those who end up becoming the primary caregivers within the family are those who live closer to the patient. But just because you are the closest to the concerned patient does not mean you do not have a life of your own. You might have other commitments like a job, marriage, or children. However, you have no choice but to find a way to balance other aspects of your life with your newfound caregiving job. Sometimes, you might have to quit your job altogether to focus more on caring for your loved one. However, in cases where you cannot quit, you will have to reduce your working hours to give you more time to carry out your caregiving duties.

Generally, your roles as a dementia caregiver include discreetly assisting your loved one with daily tasks like bathing, dressing, and grooming and helping them move from one place to another. It also involves ensuring that they eat and take their medications at the right time and taking them through the different non-drug therapies. You must also establish suitable routines with which your loved one can easily navigate their daily activities, even with memory loss. You are also responsible for calming them down when they exhibit aggressive and violent outbursts. Nevertheless, your circumstances determine the specific caregiving roles and responsibilities you perform in the life of your loved one. For example, if your loved one is still in the early dementia stage, then your roles will be less complicated. However, if they are in the mid and late stages, you have a critical role in providing them with consistent 24-hour daily care. Ultimately, your roles will be much lesser when you have the support of other family members serving as secondary caregivers.

## RISKS FOR DEMENTIA CAREGIVERS

Medical experts and researchers have labeled primary caregivers of people living with dementia as the *"invisible second patients"* (Brodaly and Donkin, 2019). This label implies that by dedicating their mind, body, and soul to caring for their loved one while ignoring the value of self-care, most caregivers eventually get to a point where they also begin to experience some physical and emotional symptoms associated with dementia.

Let's now discover the specific risk factors that can cause you, as a dementia caregiver, to become the *invisible second patient*. However, to enable more accessible and better understanding, we will classify these factors into two categories: the physical and the emotional burdens of dementia caregiving.

## THE PHYSICAL BURDENS OF DEMENTIA CAREGIVING

- **Caregiver Stress**

As a caregiver to a family member with any dementia form, you constantly experience situations that stress you in unexplainable ways. From the moment your loved one gets that diagnosis, your mind and body become overworked. You start every day by grooming the patient, helping them with a bath, and getting them dressed. You may equally serve as their chef, driver, and mobility support. You also have to calmly bear the brunt of their violent and aggressive outbursts while simultaneously helping to return to a peaceful state.

As you perform these different challenging roles, your body's flight and fight response is persistently activated, thus making your mind and body remain alert and cautious. Being in this state for an extended period puts an intense strain on your physical and psychological well-being. And when the brain recognizes this occurrence, it is bound to always react by releasing more of the body's stress hormone, which is known as *cortisol*. As more of these stress hormones get released over time, they begin to negatively affect the critical areas within the body, like your sleep patterns, and your immune, digestive, and reproductive systems (Samuels, 2020).

You probably noticed some of the warning signs of stress. They include constantly feeling tired to take part in any other activity outside your caregiving roles, getting ill more often than usual, not getting quality sleep, not eating even when you are starving, and having difficulty concentrating.

In the worst stages, caregiver stress causes a slight change in your attitudes towards the patient in your care and people in general. You quickly get irritated and angry when your loved one does something wrong or fails to complete a simple task (Alzheimer's Association, 2021). At that moment, you forget that their cognitive decline is the reason for their actions. So, you instead blame and lash out at them for their wrongdoings.

- **Caregiver Burnout**

When you fail to acknowledge and adequately address those warning signs of your caregiver stress syndrome, the high-stress levels escalate into full-blown burnout. At the burnout stage, you reach the ultimate or peak stage of your physical, mental, and emotional exhaustion. However, nobody ever gets to the point of burnout overnight; it takes a long time — which can turn into months or even years — of constant exposure to stressful experiences and unaddressed symptoms of chronic caregiver stress.

Unsurprisingly, the symptoms of caregiver burnout are usually more extreme than the signs of high-stress levels. Caregivers suffering from burnout tend to isolate and withdraw themselves entirely from the rest of the world. They navigate through their daily life with a scary sense of hopelessness. This negative life perception, coupled with their low physical energy, causes them to become less committed to caring for their dementia loved one. Hence, because they get slightly mentally detached from their identity and job, these burnout dementia caregivers will not perform effectively their caregiving duties. They quickly forget critical parts of their daily task like cooking the patient's meal or giving them the proper medication at the right time.

At the burnout stage, a caregiver also experiences massive changes in their attitude toward their loved one (Cleveland Clinic, 2019). Instead of the usual positive and caring attitude, they become pessimistic and unconcerned about the needs of the patients. It might even escalate to a point where they get so irritated or frustrated at their loved one's actions that they hurt them. For example, in a situation where the patient is having an aggressive outburst, a burnt-out caregiver might try to fight back with the same level of aggressiveness rather than being patient and calm.

- **Insomnia**

We have mentioned earlier that difficulty in getting proper and quality sleep is among the early warning signs of stress in a dementia caregiver. However, long-term dementia caregiving often complicates this particular symptom and makes it more severe.

As your loved one's dementia begins to advance to the mid and later stages, they experience worse sleep disturbances. A typical example is *sundowning*, a condition in which your dementia loved one becomes more confused, restless, and aggressive in the evening and continues in that state for the best part of the night. As their primary caregiver, you have no choice but to wake up and attend to their needs during those late hours. However, when these sleep disturbances continue for an extended period, your body's sleep-wake clock gets disrupted by the changes in your sleep patterns (Mayo Clinic, 2021). As such, your brain can no longer tell the proper sleep and wake-up time.

Eventually, you might develop insomnia, a sleep disorder quite common among dementia caregivers (Mayo Clinic, 2021). Notable signs of insomnia include difficulty dozing off and struggling to remain asleep long enough for a restorative slumber, waking up too early, and finding yourself very exhausted when you wake up. These symptoms might seem pretty uncomplicated. However, they can negatively affect your overall well-being and efficiency in providing the best care to your loved one. By denying sound and quality sleep, insomnia sucks your energy to the lowest level and dampens your mood.

Completing your daily caregiving task might be challenging without adequate physical energy and a positive mind. Not getting enough sleep weakens your immune system and puts you at greater risk of developing conditions usually associated with sleep insufficiency (Olson, 2021). Studies have shown that some dementia caregivers continue to exhibit these symptoms even after they get relieved from their caregiving roles (McCurry and Gibbons, 2019).

- **Deterioration of Physical Health**

For the longest time, medical experts and researchers have only focused on the adverse effects that long-term dementia caregiving can have on the psychological health of caregivers. However, recent studies have shown that family caregivers' physical health equally suffers a massive deterioration.

As a primary caregiver, the highly stressful experiences you encounter daily often strain your brain and body muscles. That strain on the brain often results in headaches as you forgo self-care and quality sleep to commit more time and energy to care for your loved one.

In terms of muscle strain, it might start as regular bodily pains where you feel slight aches over all your body or on specific body parts that you tend to use mostly while performing your caregiving roles. However, over time, you might notice more intense symptoms like muscle stiffness and rigidness, limiting your ability to walk properly and quickly. The physical discomfort tends to get more aggravated if you already have a history of chronic illness like arthritis.

The deadly combination of chronic caregiver stress and insomnia makes you highly susceptible to chronic health conditions like type 2 diabetes, obesity, hypertension, and other cardiovascular diseases.

- **Unexplainable Weight Loss or Weight Gain**

Chronic caregiver stress is the principal instigator of the weight changes experienced by dementia caregivers. The human body responds differently to stress. While some tend to lose weight when confronted with highly stressful experiences, others gain weight. Let's break it down to see how it works on both sides of the weight change spectrum.

The hormone *cortisol*, which is released often during periods of stress, causes a sharp spike in insulin levels and drops in blood sugar that can result in unwanted weight gain. As a result, you tend to crave more sugary and fatty foods during times of heightened stress. These foods serve as your source of comfort. So the more you eat, the more you derive pleasure from them and forget about your stress. But while these comfort food might be beneficial in lowering your stress level, they cause you to add extra pounds of weight. By failing to eat them in moderation, you might find yourself gaining a significant amount of weight at an alarming speed.

Remember, we said earlier that constant exposure to high-stress levels causes our body's flight and fight response to be persistently activated. Ideally, when the body gets programmed in this mode, it prepares to fight or flee from a threatening situation. That preparation often interferes with bodily functions like digestion and slows down its level of operation (Dolgoff, 2021). Hence, you might experience an adverse change in your appetite as you no longer do as much as you did. A poor appetite can prevent you from consuming adequate food, which is the primary way to gain weight.

Apart from stress, your roles as a dementia caregiver also leave you with little to no time for cooking or eating properly balanced meals. Sometimes, you don't even notice that you have not eaten all day because you are so preoccupied with attending to the needs of your loved one.

Now, let's pause and look at the five physical burdens of dementia caregiving that we just examined. Don't these conditions and signs appear similar to some of the dementia symptoms we examined in chapters one and two? Of course, they do. Perhaps now you can understand why researchers labeled family caregivers as the *invisible second patient*. As we begin to analyze the emotional burden, you'll get to understand the connection even better.

## THE EMOTIONAL BURDEN OF CAREGIVING

- **Mental Overload Syndrome**

As a primary caregiver, you constantly plan, multitask, perform, and obsess over the proper ways to care for your dementia loved one. In the process, your brain gets constantly bombarded with medical information about your loved one's condition, tasks from a never-ending to-do list, worrying thoughts, and emotions. However, because you are not a robot, the build-up of those elements pushes the limit of your brain's capability. Hence, you get to a point where you feel entirely overwhelmed mentally and emotionally (Cleveland Clinic, 2019).

Being overwhelmed causes you to experience different symptoms of a nervous breakdown. These symptoms could include crying uncontrollably and sometimes without a specific reason, paranoia about your loved one's condition and life in general, and having unpredictable mood swings or breathing difficulty. Sometimes, when the overload gets so overwhelming, you might consider suicide the perfect escape plan.

- **Grief**

Ideally, people associate the feeling of grief with the death of a person. However, from a broader perspective, *grief* is an emotion that comes up when we lose something. It could be a person, object, feeling, or memory.

As a caregiver, you are usually the closest person to your dementia loved one. So you witness how they gradually transform into someone you barely recognize. Unconsciously, your mind understands that you have lost your loved one as you once knew them, and grief sets in (Weitzman, 2021).

Additionally, you mourn over the fact that you will never get to achieve all those plans you made with that person. You grieve because you know there is no cure for their condition and no matter how hard you try, the ultimate end for your loved one will be death.

You grieve over how much your life has changed in ways you never planned. For example, you might have assumed the role of a caregiver at the expense of a job, college dreams, or a financial investment you have always wanted to make. The sad thing about grief in dementia caregiving is that we rarely recognize it because it's an unconscious feeling. Hence, all the pains that these feelings of grief bring mostly build up inside you and cause even more emotional damage, like anxiety and depression.

- **Anger and Frustration**

No matter how much you love that parent, spouse, or family member you care for, you will ultimately reach a limit where you lose control over your emotions and get angry at them. But you don't just get angry overnight. Instead, it is usually the build-up of long-term frustration (Cleveland Clinic, 2021).

As a dementia caregiver, you get frustrated so often in one day that you lose count. Some factors that could fuel such a high level of frustration include your loved one's uncooperative or aggressive behaviors, the absence of support from other family members, or the lack of adequate money and resources to treat the patient properly.

Of course, these reasons are enough to make even the most resilient person lose their calm and exhibit raging signs of anger. However, many caregivers feel shameful, selfish, and guilty when they lose control of their emotions and yell at their loved ones. Hence, they try as much as possible to pin down their emotions no matter how frustrated they get. Eventually, some use harmful alternatives like drinking alcohol or smoking to release their anger and calm themselves.

- **Loneliness**

Dementia caregiving, especially when done full-time, is usually a very isolating experience (Samuels, 2020). Though at the earliest stage of your loved one's condition, you might still be able to take them to social events, grocery shopping, or hang out with your friends. However, when the disease progresses into the mid stages, they experience the worst symptoms, like losing their personal inhibitions, which causes them to misbehave in public. Because of the fear of being embarrassed or judged, you often have no choice but to stay indoors with them.

The symptoms become more critical in the late stages, and your loved one demands round-the-clock support and care from you. Thus, it becomes impossible for you to interact and socialize with your peers as much as you used to. Besides, the physical and emotional burden of your caregiving roles might cause you to withdraw from those friends who even attempt to reach you. You also lose interest in the activities you used to enjoy. So, there is hardly anything to keep you company when you take a little break from your caregiving duties.

- **Depression and Anxiety**

People often say that they like to save the best for the last, but in this case, we saved the worst for last. Depression and anxiety are the most complicated and severe emotional burdens of dementia caregiving. Unfortunately, they are pretty standard among dementia caregivers today.

According to the National Alliance of Caregiving, about thirty to forty percent of dementia caregivers in the United States suffer from depression and anxiety (Samuels, 2020). In fact, studies have shown that compared to caregivers of other health conditions, dementia caregivers have higher chances of developing symptoms of depression because of the high demands of their job (Samuels, 2020). So, how can depression and anxiety affect you as a dementia caregiver? The most apparent symptom of depression is that it makes you experience persistent sadness and hopelessness. It makes you feel like your life is trash and not worth living. And because you do not see any point or purpose in life, you lose interest in everything, including your caregiving roles. Instead, the idea of committing suicide becomes more attractive to you.

Ultimately, at the stage of depression, it is almost impossible for any dementia caregiver to take care of their loved one effectively. You struggle with anxiety, internal aggressiveness, chronic tiredness, slow body reactions, and sleep disturbances, all of which puts you at a disadvantage in being an efficient caregiver.

## HOW TO COPE AND CARE FOR YOURSELF AND YOUR LOVED ONE

Finally, it's time to transform the negative energy that has been flying around since we started this chapter. As much as we might want to pretend that dementia caregiving is a gratifying experience with no negative burden, we all know that it is not. However, understanding the dynamics of the common physical and emotional burdens you are likely to experience in your caregiving journey makes it easier for you to confront them while simultaneously providing the best care to your loved one. Nevertheless, the good news is that you do not need to figure out how to tackle these burdens alone.

There are several medically reliable strategies that you, as a dementia caregiver, can employ to effectively manage each of those physical and emotional risk factors and ensure that you do not end up becoming the *invisible second patient*. Let's examine some of these strategies.

- **Taking a Temporary Leave from Work**

JANET G. CRUZ

Having a traditional job while simultaneously caring for a dementia patient is the perfect risk factor for caregiver burnout and mental overload. While the perfect solution to reduce that risk will be to resign from our jobs as full-time dementia care-givers, many of us cannot afford such luxury. Notwithstanding, a temporary work leave is an excellent alternative to quitting your job.

You already understand the symptoms of caregiver burnout and mental overload. Hence, when you notice the warning signs, you can take a temporary leave from your job for a certain period. In the United States, employees covered under the federal Family and Medical Leave Act can take a temporary although unpaid leave of up to 12 weeks to cater to their sick loved ones (Mayo Clinic, 2021). By taking only a few weeks off work, you can improve your mental health by practicing the right self-care strategies. At that same time, you will have more time to take care of your loved one.

- **Setting Attainable and Realistic Goals**

Because we desperately want to help our loved ones overcome their condition as much as possible, many dementia caregivers often make the mistake of setting unrealistic goals. We want to do everything for them — cleaning, cooking, driving them to the hospital, or taking them for walks.

Sometimes these unrealistic expectations might come from other family members who only serve as secondary caregivers.

They may expect you to quit your job, leave your house to move in with the dementia patient and do all the in-house chores and outdoor errands. Such unreasonable goals only increase your susceptibility to mental overload and burnout. Thus, when setting your caregiving goals, it is crucial that you only focus on what you can comfortably offer regarding your abilities, emotional capability, time, and financial resources. In cases where you have significant and complicated tasks, you could break them into smaller steps and focus on completing each step, one at a time.

- **Accepting Help**

Most caregivers often struggle to ask or accept help from other people, especially when the person is not directly related to them. However, as a dementia caregiver, you must understand that you and your family cannot do it alone. Thus, when a friend or neighbor offers to help through physical or financial assistance, you should welcome them with open hands. Of course, it might be hard to trust anyone to take care of your vulnerable loved one. However, there are situations where you would be unavailable, like when you are busy at work. In such cases, your best option is to ask a trustworthy family member or friend to take care of your loved one until you return.

To calm your mind, ensure you give them all the information they need to deliver their caregiving duties more efficiently. Such help can also come in handy when you feel burnout and desperately need a break from your caregiving duties.

## CONNECTING WITH THE RIGHT SUPPORT GROUPS

Because of how common dementia is today, many caregivers from different parts of the world have come together to form countless groups and communities that can serve as a perfect support system for other dementia caregivers.

In these groups, you will find caregivers who have experienced or are currently dealing with the same challenges as you. Thus, by joining such communities of people who share the same identity as you, you tend to fit in quickly, and in no time, you will find yourself making new friends who truly understand what it feels like to be in your shoes. With such a supportive network, you can easily overcome loneliness and isolation. But apart from socializing, the members of these support groups usually share real-life stories about their caregiving journey. As you read or listen to these stories, you learn new tips or tricks to help tackle the challenges you encounter as a caregiver. These stories can also serve as a source of hope and inspiration. The best part is that you get to ask questions or vent about your experiences as a caregiver without being judged.

So how do you find the right support group? Most of these support groups are freely available online. So all you have to do is check across different social media platforms, especially Facebook and join the one that best suits your circumstances as a dementia caregiver.

## FOCUSING ON YOUR PERSONAL HEALTH

We have already established that dementia caregiving often denies one the opportunity to get quality sleep. However, you can monitor your loved one's sleep pattern and use that information to design an effective sleeping routine for yourself. However, if you have insomnia, it would be best to see a doctor who can recommend suitable options to cure your sleeping disorder.

In addition to getting adequate sleep, you must stay physically active. Doing a simple cardio workout at least 3 to 4 times a week can increase your muscle strength and overall health. Your diet is also an essential part of your personal health. To prevent either weight gain or loss, you must stick to a healthy diet and drink plenty of water to stay hydrated. Also, if you suspect that you are already exhibiting some of the symptoms of depression and anxiety that we mentioned earlier, then it would be best to consult a therapist as fast as you can.

## EMBRACING THAT SENSE OF PURPOSE IN YOUR CAREGIVING JOURNEY

No matter the number of physical and emotional burdens that come with dementia caregiving, it remains a rewarding and fulfilling job for many family caregivers across the world. As a primary caregiver, your daily assistance and selfless services to your loved one make a significant difference in the quality of your loved one's life. Although their condition makes it impossible for them to understand your gestures or express gratitude, you should embrace the notion that you are committing a significant part of your life to care for your loved one.

So what does that make you? The best family — friend, spouse, son, or daughter — anyone can ever have! Hence, you should feel valued and fulfilled that your dedication to your caregiving job has helped ensure that your dementia loved one gets to spend the last years of their life in the best way possible. Ultimately, the harsh reality about dementia caregiving is that nobody is born ready for this job. Except for those who are professionally trained caregivers, most of us unexpectedly get thrown into this life commitment with no prior knowledge or skill. Thus, we are bound to experience the severe physical and emotional burden that targets explicitly the primary caregiver.

Thankfully, you better understand now how your loved one's dementia condition is to transform your life as a caregiver. Thus, instead of being caught unarmed when the harsh reality hits and almost makes you give up, you are now equipped with the perfect strategies to specifically manage these physical and emotional burdens. To a large extent, you have lower chances of developing the *invisible second patient* syndrome. Isn't that incredible?

# PLAN OF ACTION

> "Caregiving has no second agendas or hidden motives. The care is given from love for the joy of giving without expectations, no strings attached."
>
> – Gary Zukav

*W*e have spent the last six chapters of this book exploring the critical details of dementia from three major perspectives. To gain a full understanding of dementia, we began by evaluating the perspectives of medical professionals and researchers. We also examined all aspects related to the development and management of this condition including its causes, the dangers or risk factors, symptoms, stages, and treatments. Then, we switched to the patient's perspective, through which we understood the dynamics of dementia, specifically from your loved one's point of view. Finally, we shifted our focus to you, the caregiver, and analyzed your caregiving roles and the physical and emotional burden that every dementia caregiver is bound to encounter.

Without a doubt, we have provided you with an exhaustive education about your loved one's dementia diagnosis. Hence, you are now equipped with adequate knowledge about your loved one's disease and your roles and duties as their caregivers. However, having adequate knowledge about dementia is not enough to conquer the challenges that lie before you and your dementia loved one. To effectively navigate, excel and survive through every phase of your journey as a dementia caregiver, your newfound knowledge needs to be coupled with the right action plan. And that's what we'll be doing in this chapter — creating a plan of action that outlines and analyzes practical ideas and strategies to help you effectively tackle some of the biggest challenges ahead of you in this caregiving journey.

Rather than just focusing on one section, this action plan contains effective strategies and tips for seven (7) broad areas of dementia caregiving which include dealing with dementia denial, staying in control as a caregiver, preventing stress and patient abuse, engaging with compassion, creating a healthier home environment, engaging with other family members, and finally, finding the suitable activities for your loved one. Based on the long list we just made, it is evident that we are in for a long and adventurous ride. So get yourself in a very relaxed position and let's get started!

## TIPS FOR DEALING WITH DENIAL

We have mentioned several times in the previous chapters that a dementia diagnosis triggers a lot of negative emotions — like shock, anger, frustration, and sadness — in both the patient and their entire family. However, beyond these typical emotions, there is one dangerous reaction that most dementia patients and even their families tend to showcase once the dementia diagnosis gets confirmed. It's *denial.*

To escape the fear and devastation of facing the truth of their condition, your loved one might prefer to live in denial. However, since they do not want to believe that they will never get to live that much-anticipated happy and healthy life in their old age, they opt for the easiest route, which is to deny the existence of their disease. However, a denial reaction from your loved one is dangerous and detrimental to both, themselves and you, their caregiver. When your loved one is in denial about their dementia condition, they quickly reject any help offered. They refuse to follow the guidelines and precautions from their healthcare provider concerning managing their condition. It would be impossible to get them to quit their job, reduce working hours, retire from driving, or even accept you as their primary caregiver. Notwithstanding how determined your loved one might be to continuously live in denial of their condition, there are steps you can take to convince them to understand and accept the reality of their dementia with a positive mindset. Let's examine these steps.

- **Take a Bold Step and have that Much-Needed Conversation**

Ideally, when a dementia patient is in denial about their condition, discussing that subject in their presence becomes wholly forbidden. Thus, the only way you can kick-start this journey to helping them gain acceptance is to address the elephant in the room. Then, you can watch out to detect when they are in a better mood to discuss the subject. To avoid intense resistance from them, you have to be discreet at first and then gradually open up on the topic.

You must stay calm and listen to them when they react by denying the diagnosis. You can gently try to reconstruct their perspective about dementia by providing them with reliable facts about the disease. Instead of bombarding them with information you got from the Internet, you can make them watch a TV program or movie related to dementia. It could also be a book or leaflets on dementia. Their curiosity heightens as you continuously chat about dementia and supply them with important information about the condition. However, the truth is that underneath all their fearless showcase of denial, your loved one still cares a lot about their health and overall well-being. As such, they cannot reject your offer to educate them about a disease that is about to transform their entire life.

- **Be Positive and Pledge Your Support**

Studies have shown that many dementia patients who hide under the shadow of denial often do so because their minds are filled with thoughts about the adverse effects that dementia will have on their life.

As a caregiver, you are responsible for shifting your loved one's negative perspective into a more positive one. Let them know that although there is currently no verified cure for dementia, treatments are available to help them manage the symptoms for a very long time. Drawing from that information, you must emphasize that the best way for them to get proper care is to accept this new normal. Doing so creates a sense of urgency that can make them want to start the treatment process almost immediately.

You can also change your loved one's mind about dementia into a more positive one by pledging your unwavering support. Make the person see and believe that you will still be there with them, no matter how challenging your condition is in the next 10 to 15 years. You can even start showcasing that support from the early stages of your loved one's dementia by attending necessary medical appointments with them.

- **Don't Try to Force It**

No matter how committed you are to ensuring that your loved one overcomes their denial phase, you must be empathetic when approaching them. Their strong resistance might counter your first few attempts. Please don't force them to accept their reality when such happens. Instead, you can get their health-care provider to do the convincing. Since medical experts are well aware of the emotional effects that getting a dementia diagnosis can have on patients, they will know how best to help your loved one understand and acknowledge the reality of their condition. On the other hand, it could be that your loved one needs time to fully accept that frightening diagnosis (Alzheimer's' Society, 2021). So until that time comes, you should focus more on understanding their feeling and offering them support than trying to persuade them into acceptance.

- **Focus on Yourself**

Your loved one is not the only one likely to react in denial after a dementia diagnosis. In the beginning, you might also find yourself trying so hard to deny that your parents, spouse, or relative is experiencing critical physical, mental, and emotional changes that you could not control. But how do you push your loved one out of the denial phase when you are also falling deep into its trap? You must first understand that it is only natural to feel that way because you genuinely care about and love this patient. Once you have acknowledged that fact, you can start shifting your perspective by learning more about your loved one's dementia condition.

Before reading this book, you probably thought that getting diagnosed with dementia was an automatic death sentence for your loved one. However, based on what we have explored in the previous chapters of this book, you will now agree that your loved one still has the chance to live for several years in good health. To achieve this important milestone, they need to kick start either or both medication and non-medication treatments as quickly as possible.

## TIPS FOR STAYING IN CONTROL

As a caregiver to a dementia patient, it is imperative for you to always be in control of your loved one's daily activities. As they advance into their condition's mid and later stages, they become more dependent on you to survive each day. Thus, you cannot afford to lose control.

Challenging factors — like violent resistance from your loved one when you offer to help and frustrations from the daily physical, mental and financial stress of caregiving — are often the major culprits that prevent you from staying in control. Here are a few tips to help you overcome these challenges and remain in power as your loved one's primary caregiver.

- **Adopt Effective Planning Techniques**

In the world of dementia, planning involves a critical process of breaking down the caregiving responsibilities of your loved one into smaller and more manageable tasks. As a caregiver, there are several planning techniques that you can adopt to feel more in control and less stressed. One of the best techniques involves creating a stable routine plan for your dementia loved one.

To create an incredible routine plan, you must ensure that your loved one follows a consistent time for bathing, grooming, dressing, eating, taking medication, and doing other daily activities. Through frequent repetition, the routine is implanted or stored in their long-term memory and they even start to anticipate what each day will bring. So, even without your supervision, you might notice the patient moving swiftly from one activity to another. That sense of order and the ability to correctly predict their daily life pattern makes your loved one feel more at ease and less likely to be anxious or agitated.

Apart from creating stable routine plans, you also have to make a daily to-do list where you write the tasks you want to complete and the timeframe within which you should get them done. Additionally, you need a system to give you constant reminders on essential tasks you need to complete. For example, such obligations could involve a medical appointment or giving medications to a dementia person. I invite you to download the bonus gift I have for you that will help you set up a complete action plan.

- **Involve Your Loved One**

No matter the dementia stage your loved one might be at, you must involve them in the planned routine as much as their condition permits. For instance, you can include them in more manageable household tasks like folding laundry, washing dishes, selecting outfits, etc. Of course, they may need help to complete the job correctly. However, those activities help them feel more involved in their care. Thus, you must commend them for their efforts and reinforce their sense of self-worth (American Seniors Housing Association, 2022).

## TIPS FOR PREVENTING CAREGIVER STRESS AND PATIENT ABUSE

Your mind is bound to be in a constant state of hyperactiveness when you are a caregiver providing round-the-clock care and support to a dementia patient while simultaneously taking care of your family and personal obligations. Though you might not realize it, everything you do requires the help of your mind. Hence, it is always filled with thoughts, plans, and emotions, often hostile. And, like we said when discussing brain overload and burnout, it gets to a point where this incoming information gets too much, and you start *losing* your mind because it can no longer handle the mental and emotional burden.

At that stage, you might react negatively towards your loved one to the point where you begin to attack them in resentment. However, one significant way to prevent such grave consequences is to ensure that your mind gets free from the mental and emotional burden it is subjected to daily. And that is where the powerful meditation tool comes in to save the day.

- **Meditation Tool**

Meditation is a self-care tool that lets you hit the pause button to escape your reality and regain control of your mind temporarily. In taking control through meditation, you draw your mind back from its wandering state and ground it in the present moment, where you can reflect on the thoughts, emotions, and every other element immersed within your mind.

As you reflect while meditating, you also become aware of your most hidden and pent-up thoughts and emotions, some of which you probably never knew you had confined in your mind. Consequently, gaining that heightened self-awareness makes it easier to acknowledge and filter out those negative emotions and thoughts contributing to your daily stress and draining spirit. The more you continuously filter out those harmful elements, the more your mind gets elevated to a very calm state. And when that happens, you experience a higher degree of inner peace, joy, and confidence because your mind is free from any mental and emotional burden.

Having an overall sense of calm and contentment plays a significant role in ensuring that your loved one is given the best possible care. Even when you get faced with aggressiveness and violence from your dementia patient, you efficiently exercise an admirable level of self-control. So, isn't it incredible that with just one self-care tool, you can enjoy all of these benefits — mind decluttering, stress management, self-awareness, and, most importantly, a greater sense of calmness and happiness? Of course, it is. However, the pertinent question remains, "How do you practice meditation as a dementia caregiver?"

There are various meditation techniques such as yoga, tai chi, and qi gong currently available. However, these exercises often involve a lot of commitment, especially in time. Unfortunately, time is a luxury that you cannot afford as a caregiver single-handedly tending to the needs of your dementia loved one, your family, as well as your obligations. Nevertheless, there are other means to practice meditation. In fact, you can gain the benefits of meditation without doing any particular body movement. Sound unbelievable?

Here are some helpful tips on practicing meditation in the most basic ways and gaining all of its benefits.

### 1. Sit Quietly Without Doing Anything

An elementary yet potent form of mediation involves sitting still without doing anything for a short period. How you sit or place your hands does not matter in that situation, so you should not worry about it. What matters most is sitting still in a tranquil and calm area. It could be in an empty room within your house or outside where you get direct access to nature. As you sit, try to shut your mind from thinking about anything.

Of course, sitting still in silence without doing anything might sound quite strange. However, the stillness and silence are actually influential on your mind. It is putting a *purposeful pause* on your hyperactive mind that has been thinking, analyzing, and figuring out things throughout the day (Crumpler, 2022). So, rather than thinking of the stress, tasks, and worries, you intentionally force your mind to take a break and focus on the present moment of *"nothingness."*

During your first few attempts, you might need help to completely stop your mind from wandering. However, as you become more consistent in your practice, it will become much easier to bring your mind to a pause and shed off those worries and stress.

The best thing about this form of meditation is that you can do it as many times in a day as you want. In fact, once you feel like you are emotionally overwhelmed, find a quiet place and sit in silence. In less than 10 minutes, you will get that calming effect your mind needs.

### 2. Focus on Your Breathing

Remember, in your first few attempts at meditating, it would be difficult to stop your mind from wandering or drifting from the present moment. Focusing on your breathing during meditation is the perfect solution to overcome the challenge of your wandering mind. So here is how it works.

As you sit still in a quiet location, slowly inhale and exhale. You are expected to focus entirely on how you breathe in and out. You can even count out loud to make it easier. So you inhale and exhale, then count "1". Again, you breathe in and out, then count "2."

Continue with that same pattern until you count to 10. At that point, you will be surprised at how fast your mind has shifted from your perceived stress and emotional burden to a more relaxed and calm state.

### 3. Pay Attention to Sounds

The best thing about meditation is that there are many opportunities to practice it when different calming and subtle sounds surround you. So, for instance, you are taking a shower, and your mind is in chaos. In that quiet bathroom, you can practice a 5 to 10-minute meditation. All you have to do is focus on the water splashing on your body to shift your mind from that chaotic state to the point where you are no longer thinking about anything but that present moment (Abrahms, 2020). Several other sounds can serve as your focal point to practice meditation. It could come from a dog barking, a lawnmower running, or even the sound of rain pouring down from the sky.

### 4. Take a Walk

Who says you have to be seated still to practice meditation effectively? Nobody! So, when you have someone to look over your dementia loved one for some time, you can quickly walk around the neighborhood. As you walk, you should observe your steps on the sidewalk. You can even count your steps out loud to keep you focused. In addition to monitoring your walking steps on the sidewalk, you can look around and consciously pay attention to your surroundings.

Ultimately, you, as a dementia caregiver, can incorporate the practice of meditation into your daily routine. By doing so, you get to put a purposeful pause in your life for just a few minutes and then carry on with the rest of your day. Always remember that there is no restriction; you can meditate as many times in a day as you want. So the very moment you feel like you are mentally and emotionally overwhelmed, take a break to meditate and regain control over your chaotic mind.

## TIPS FOR ENGAGING WITH COMPASSION

Some of the most significant challenges you will face as a dementia caregiver come from the lack of proper communication between you and your loved one.

Due to the deterioration in their memory and language skills, dementia patients often find it impossible to express their needs and feelings clearly. And the fact that nobody understands them or grants their needs makes them violent, aggressive, and anxious. But we know that this frustration is usually not one-sided. As a caregiver who is genuinely committed to improving the quality of your loved one's life, you also cannot help but feel angry and frustrated when your loved one is not communicating but showcasing aggressive behaviors and resisting your offer of help. However, here are some vital tips that can help you engage and share with your loved one most compassionately, even when they are being aggressive and unwilling.

You should:

- Respect your loved one's personal space and allow them to enjoy as much independence as their condition permits. For example, if they can still pick out their outfits by themselves, let them do it with no intervention on your part.

- Always try to engage them in a two-way conversation when they are in their best moods. It does not matter how long the discussion lasts; make sure they understand you are genuinely interested in knowing what they think and feel.

- When your loved one is frustrated and uncooperative, speak to them calmly and reassure them of your continuous support and loyalty. Always show them your empathetic side.

- If you notice that the patient does not seem to remember or recognize who you are to them, gently remind them without making them feel dumb or mentally ill.

- Spend as much time as you can with them. Refrain from trying to force them to communicate with words during those times. Instead, the two of you can engage in fun and exciting activities that the patient enjoys. With time, they will become more comfortable with you.

## TIPS FOR CREATING A HEALTHIER HOME ENVIRONMENT

Recent research studies have shown that dementia patients receiving home care tend to live longer, healthier, and happier lives than those in medical facilities. However, before your loved one can enjoy such incredible benefits, the home in which they live has to be as dementia-friendly as possible. Therefore, a dementia-friendly home needs to be modified and conditioned to ensure the safety and independence of people with dementia.

Now that you understand how your loved one's mobility and balance issues increase their risk of falls as they progress through the mid stages of dementia, it is important to be especially aware and prepared. The deterioration in their memory often makes them more prone to wander and abandon their activity halfway. Such situations could have significant consequences and even risk the patient's life. So how can you and the rest of the family modify your loved one's home into a dementia-friendly environment?

You must:

- Scan the entire house and eliminate every unnecessary item taking up space.

- Clear out things that your loved one is likely to trip over when walking, the small rugs or electrical cords on the ground. Curtains and rugs with complicated patterns that can confuse a dementia patient when moving around the house should also get disposed into the trash bin.

- If there are stairs in the home, you should ensure that it is equipped with at least one handrail (National Institute of Aging, 2021). Then tack down a firm carpet and paint the edges of the stairs so that your loved one can differentiate one stair from the other.

- Install safety detectors like smoke alarms, fall monitors, and carbon monoxide alarms strategically in the house. Doing so will help alert you in case your loved one is at risk.

- Ensure proper lighting is present in every room or outdoor area around the house where the patient is likely to move around.

- Place signs, pictures, and sticky notes around the house to help the patients identify where their things belong or the purpose of each room.

- Always pack up inedible household products — like cleaning and laundry materials — and lock them in a closet that is not accessible to your loved one.

## HOW TO STOP YOUR LOVED ONE FROM WANDERING AND GETTING LOST?

Did you know that six in every ten dementia patients are bound to wander off accidentally and get lost at least once? These statistics are clear proof that almost every person with dementia stands a high risk of wandering off. Since we are well aware of the immense and perhaps life-threatening danger associated with an aged dementia person wandering and getting lost, our best option is to lower these risks.

Here are some preventive measures you can take to protect your loved one from wandering and getting lost.

- Equip your home with safety devices like warning bells on the doors or a monitoring device that sends an alert when the house's main entrance gets opened. You can even place a pressure-sensitive rug in front of the door or beside your loved one's bedside to signal you when they make any movement.

- Use a fence or hedges to surround the entire house, patio, or another outdoor area that your loved one tends to visit.

- If the patient is still living alone, ensure you check in on him/her as frequently as possible. You can also inform the neighbors about the person's condition so that they can check in on your behalf and contact you if they notice any strange thing about your loved one.

- Avoid taking the person to an overcrowded shopping mall or park area.

- Do not leave the dementia patient alone at home or in the car.

- Always ensure that you take care of the patient's basic needs — like food, water, and toileting — so they have no excuse to go out.

## TIPS FOR ENGAGING WITH YOUR FAMILY

When discussing the different coping strategies for caregivers in the previous chapter, we emphasized that no matter how competent and determined you might be, it will be impossible and perhaps suicidal for you to take on every caregiving-related responsibility by yourself. Hence, you need to seek help and accept it when others try to offer it. Although you might not realize it, it is normal for other family members to be unaware of the responsibilities and stressful situations you go through as the primary caregiver. Rather than just expecting them to understand over time, it is your responsibility to enlighten them and help them realize caregiving is not a job for one person to handle. But getting them to understand is only the beginning. You also have to find a way to make them share in the caregiving responsibilities. So, for instance, you could call for a family meeting or get the oldest family member to do so. Before going into that meeting, you must ensure that you already have a list of all the current and anticipated caregiving responsibilities. Then you present that list to every family member and allow them to pick a choice that suits their abilities, financial resources, and emotional capacity.

Eventually, the roles might get shared unevenly. Still, you will have successfully built a supportive family caregiving team who will ensure you never get to the stage of burning out or losing your mind. So, imagine that you have different helpers for external obligations like driving and accompanying the patient to medical appointments, researching the best treatment and care facilities, and catering to legal and financial responsibilities. Your life as a caregiver will be much easier, and you will be able to provide the best hands-on care for your loved one. Also, you will not be overburdened by the financial stress generated by your loved one's disease. Every family member will have to contribute, depending on how much they can afford. The whole family can also source external financial assistance from non-profit organizations.

## TIPS FOR FINDING THE RIGHT ACTIVITIES FOR YOUR LOVED ONE

Apart from sharing caregiving responsibilities, you and other family members can collectively develop ideas for fun, but cognitively challenging activities for your dementia loved one.

Today, we have countless recommended activities for improving the symptoms of dementia patients. Hence, making the right choice for your loved one is often a challenging task which is why you need the help of other family members. Like you, they also have adequate knowledge of the patient's interests, hobbies, and preferences. Nevertheless, there are specific steps you can take if you truly want to find the right set of activities that can help your loved one feel productive and confident in their ability. And the best way to start the selection process is to consider where your loved one's significant interests lay — before their diagnosis, what activities did they enjoy the most? What specific task were they good at performing around the house?

Once you map out these interests, you find activities related to those interests. So, for example, if your loved one used to be great at organizing things around the house, you can easily select activities that enable them to manage things and feel a sense of accomplishment. However, you must ensure that the selected activities are neither too easy nor too difficult for the patient's current cognitive ability (Stringfellow, 2019). If they find it too easy, they might feel insulted or easily bored. But if your loved one cannot complete the selected activities successfully, they might feel disappointed or even consider themselves failures.

To make this process easier for you and your family, we have compiled some of the most productive but failure-free proven activities your loved one might enjoy. Remember that you must keep trying different activities until you find the one that your loved one enjoys the most. So, let's check them out!

### 1. Activities Based on Life Skills

Most caregivers believe that the activities for dementia patients have to be planned, like games or leisure activities. However, the best activities could require your loved one to take part in their daily living skills. For example, these activities could involve holding their toothbrush and brushing themselves, folding the napkins, setting or clearing the table, selecting their outfit for the day, or even watering the plants around the house (Stringfellow, 2019). Of course, they would not be able to complete these activities independently, but with your guidance, and perhaps with other family members' support, you can make it work.

Apart from keeping them happily and satisfactorily engaged, these activities fill your loved one with a sense of accomplishment and confidence. They feel like they are contributing massively to the successful running of the household. No matter how well or poorly they perform those activities, you must endeavor to commend their efforts and make them feel good about their hard work. Encouragement plays an important part in how your loved one may feel.

## 2. Solving Picture Puzzles

If your loved one is someone who once enjoyed solving puzzles, this activity might be the perfect pick for them. However, you can make DIY picture puzzles rather than getting them the traditional jigsaw puzzle which might be more difficult. All you have to do is print and laminate a copy of your loved one's favorite photo. It could be a photo of themselves or a general family photo.

Once you have laminated the photo, cut it into as many puzzle-piece-shaped pieces as you think your loved one might be able to handle (DailyCaring Editorial Team, 2022). When they are in the right mood to play, present the puzzle to them and cheer them on as they try to solve it.

## 3. Coin Sorting

Coin sorting can be a fun and thrilling activity for dementia patients who once enjoyed organizing things. In this case, you gather all your loose change, then get small glasses or bowls into which your loved one can sort those coins.

Although this activity might seem very simple to an average person, your loved one might find it very complex; thus, if they manage to complete it well, they are bound to get excited and feel valuable and confident.

The materials to be sorted don't have to be coins. They could be fabrics of different colors and textures if your loved one used to be someone interested in sowing or any other fabric craft. If they were the fixer or the go-to handyman, screws, bolts, and nuts might be a better option.

Here are some other planned activities you and the other family members can engage in with your dementia loved one.

You can:

- Create a memory box or bag with them by allowing them to pick out random items that remind them of their memories. It could be anything — books, clothes, treasure items, scented products, etc.

- Listen to their favorite music and dance with them.

- Write brief notes on cards and pass them around yourselves.

- Organize family events like a game night or an outdoor picnic with them. In organizing a family picnic, you must consider the unique needs of your loved one. For example, you can provide camping chairs instead of everyone sitting on the ground to ensure the patient does not have trouble sitting down throughout the picnic.

- Go for short walks in areas with no branches or other obstacles that could prevent your loved one from moving around freely and get some exercise. You can visit parks or even take short walks around your neighborhood in the mornings.

Ultimately, we must understand that your loved one might not even enjoy the selected activities despite all your efforts. However, it's completely okay, so you should not beat yourself up over it. Instead, you can easily switch to something else you believe they might enjoy. Finding suitable activities for your loved one is often a lengthy trial and error process, but eventually, you will find the right choices, and seeing your loved one happy will be worth the long search.

On that cheerful note, we have come to the end of this rather long and adventurous chapter. Notwithstanding, it was worth every second spent exploring because you have now obtained adequate knowledge on how to survive through some of the most challenging phases of your caregiving journey. But before we wrap up this book, we must discover one last puzzle. So, are you good to go on this final treasure hunt?

Let's begin!

# GETTING HELP / RESOURCES

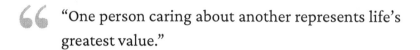

"One person caring about another represents life's greatest value."

– Jim Rohn

*J*n the last chapter, there is no doubt that we formulated an effective action plan to guarantee success in your caregiving journey. However, in this last lap, we will be making the final yet critical touches to getting you fully ready for the never-ending challenges of dementia caregiving. As primary caregivers, many of us are often unaware of the amazing resources and services available to make our jobs easier and less burdensome. Thus, our goal in this chapter is to uncover and examine those available sources of help as well as where and how you can get them. However, to enable better understanding, we will classify these helpful resources and services into two categories: getting help for yourself as a primary caregiver and getting help for your dementia loved one.

In each category, we have three sections. Under your category as a primary caregiver, we will discuss how you can get adequate help assessing your stress levels, getting temporary breaks from caregiving responsibilities, and connecting with an effective support system. On the part of your loved one, we will uncover how you can find the right information sources about their condition, how to manage their memory deterioration, and the appropriate professional caregiving services to adopt for them when the time is right.

## GETTING HELP FOR YOURSELF AS A PRIMARY CAREGIVER

### 1. Caregiver Stress Assessment

Although we identified the most noticeable symptoms of caregiver stress and burnout in chapter six, there is a high possibility that you still find it difficult to detect clearly when your stress levels exceed normal and approach the point of burnout. Fortunately, you don't have to visit a healthcare expert before confirming if you truly suffer from caregiver stress or burnout.

Currently, medical experts and organizations in the field of dementia care have designed standardized questionnaires, quizzes, and checklists with which you, as a primary caregiver, can assess or measure the level of your stress or burnout (American Psychology Association, 2020).

In most cases, these questionnaires, quizzes, and checklists contain a fixed list of the common feelings and symptoms experienced by dementia caregivers. Then, beside each stated symptom or feeling, you assign a score to describe the extent to which you are experiencing those symptoms. Using numbers or scores is mostly common in stress assessment quizzes. However, for questionnaires or checklists, you will most likely have options like *"Never, Sometimes, Often, or Rarely."* And all you have to do is select the specific options that best describe the extent to which you experience each of the identified stress signs.

After completing the assessment, you also get adequate information about where you belong on the stress spectrum and the specific stress management strategies that would be most effective for your condition. The best thing about these assessment instruments is that they are quick and easy to complete. Thus, you can fill them almost every day if you wish. Doing so will enable you to determine how your stress levels change over a particular period.

Where and how do we find these standardized caregiver stress assessment instruments? They are mostly available online, but you can always download them and print them in hard paper copies. Here are some of the best online caregiver stress assessment instruments and the website addresses with which you can access them.

### 1. AARP's Caregiver Stress Quiz

https://www.aarp.org/health/healthy-living/info-2022/self-care-quiz.html

### 2. Alzheimer's Society of Canada's Caregiver Stress Assessment Checklist

https://bit.ly/caregiver-assessment-checklist

### 3. American Psychological Association's Caregiver Self-Assessment Questionnaire

https://www.healthinaging.org/tools-and-tips/caregiver-self-assessment-questionnaire

### 4. Kingston Caregiver Stress Scale (KCSS)

http://www.kingstonscales.org/caregiver-stress-scale.html

### 5. National Caregivers Library's Caregiver Self-Assessment Questionnaire

https://bit.ly/caregiver-self-assessment

## ADOPTING RESPITE CARE FOR TEMPORARY RELIEF FROM CAREGIVING DUTIES

If, after using any of the assessment instruments that we identified in the previous section, you figured out that your stress level is pretty high, self-care is one of the management strategies that the assessment agency will recommend to you. And taking temporary relief from your caregiving responsibilities is one of the best ways to get adequate self-care as a dementia caregiver. But how can your loved one survive without their primary caregiver? In this case, the easiest choice is to get other family members or friends to take over for a few days or weeks, depending on how long you want to spend on your break. However, only some of us have family members or friends with the time, energy, or emotional capability to properly handle our caregiving responsibilities. Thus, this challenge leaves us with one last resort — *respite care.*

Respite care is a service that enables your dementia loved one to receive the best professional care available in a safe, welcoming atmosphere while you, their primary caregiver, take a break for a few hours, days, or even months (Alzheimer's Association, 2021). Nonetheless, with your loved one in respite care, you can comfortably and peacefully enjoy yourself through different self-care activities. It could be shopping, visiting the spa, traveling with friends you have not seen for ages, taking part in activities like swimming, dancing, and exercising which are fun; or maybe just taking some time off to recharge.

So, let's consider two major types of respite care services you can employ for your loved one when you need to take a temporary break from your responsibilities as a caregiver.

- **Home Health Services**

Hiring home health services is a great option for respite care, especially if your temporary break lasts moderately long. Also, if you find yourself in a job that occupies most of your day, then this option could be a perfect arrangement. It does not matter if your loved one is still at the earliest stages of the disease. Nevertheless, this respite option involves employing one or more home health providers with adequate experience in caring for dementia patients to provide the best professional assistance to your loved one. Generally, home health providers offer a wide range of medical and non-medical care services. Non-medical services such as personal care, homemaker duties, and companionship are becoming increasingly popular (Alzheimer's Association, 2021).

Regarding companion services, the hired home health provider dedicates 24-hour supervision or consistent visitations to your loved one. The personal care services involve helping the patients with activities like toileting, bathing, dressing, and eating while the homemaker services cover their housekeeping, grocery shopping, and cooking tasks.

In contrast, a home health provider's medical services involve more complicated duties like giving injections, wound care, physical therapy, and treatments for minor infections (Alzheimer's Association, 2021). Thus, as a primary caregiver, you must ensure that only licensed healthcare professionals are employed to care for your loved ones' medical needs at home.

Finding the right home health providers to replace you as a primary caregiver can be complicated. Hence, it is always helpful to ask for recommendations from experts like your loved one's primary physician or friends and families with first-hand experience with these home care services.

- **Adult Daycare Centers**

Adult daycare centers are like part-time assisted living facilities. These centers help take over your position as a primary caregiver for about seven to ten hours daily during the weekdays, although some daycare centers also work on weekends.

The overall function of an adult daycare center is to provide your loved one with a chance to meet with other people like them and participate in fun social activities that can slow the progression of their brain disease. Beyond that primary function, they may also provide medical services, personal care, or behavioral therapy. But the provision of these services varies from one center to another. So, before enrolling your loved one in an adult day care center, you must make all the necessary inquiries about their services to ensure that it suits the special needs of your loved one.

## BUILDING YOUR OWN SUPPORT GROUP

As much as every caregiver would love to take frequent temporary breaks from their caregiving responsibilities, respite care is not something that we can all easily afford as often and as long as we may want. However, having a robust support system outside your family members and friends can greatly complement your irregular caregiving break. You would recall that while discussing the caregiver's perspective of dementia, we identify connecting with the right support group as an effective caregiver's stress management strategy.

Joining an ideal caregiver support group allows you to connect with fellow caregivers who experience the same daily struggles as you and can truly relate to your emotions and feelings. They make you see and accept that you are not alone on the caregiving path, but rather you have many companions equally journeying with you (Smith, 2022). Additionally, you get to acquire invaluable lessons and knowledge from other caregivers as they share their struggles and how they managed to overcome some or all of them.

There are two major ways to find the best support groups. You can search for one in your local community or join an online support group if it is not convenient for you to go out often and attend physical meetings regularly. Nevertheless, these two types of support groups are equally beneficial.

While local support groups allow you to form intimate relationships with a limited number of dementia caregivers, online support groups give you access to caregivers from different parts of the world from the comfort of your home and at the most convenient time (Smith, 2022). No matter how rare your loved one's dementia type might be, you will always find a caregiver dealing with the same dementia type in an online support group. Also, if there is ever a case of an emergency concerning your loved one's condition, you can always contact an online support group and get the quick help you need.

Here are some of the best online caregiver support groups you can consider joining. But you must first note that most of these support groups are available on Facebook.

1. Family Caregiver Alliance (FCA)
2. The Purple Sherpa Basecamp (Dementia Family Caregiver Support Group)
3. Caregiver Support Community
4. AgingCare's Caregiver Forum
5. Caring For Elderly Parents
6. Caring for Spouses with Dementia
7. Caregivers Connect
8. Caregivers Assist Support Group
9. Caregiver Hub Support Group
10. Working Daughter

## GETTING HELP FOR YOUR DEMENTIA LOVED ONE

- **Finding the Right Dementia Caregiver Resources**

Dementia caregiving is a journey of ongoing education and understanding. Since you are not a certified medical expert or healthcare provider, there will never be a point where you figure out everything about your loved one's condition. More often than usual, you will encounter situations where your dementia loved one begins to showcase strange signs and symptoms that will leave you confused and clueless about the right steps. Hence, because we are learning on the job, every caregiver must do adequate research and keep educating themselves about their loved one's condition.

You will be surprised that every time you start researching, you find new details you had no idea of beforehand. However, finding the right sources to provide quality dementia information can be quite challenging. But, like usual, our goal is to make this journey as easy as possible for you. Thus, we have compiled a list of ten top national organizations that will offer credible and updated information and other resources about dementia and your role as a caregiver. So, here we go...

*1. Family Caregiver Alliance*

*2. Dementia Action Alliance: Discovery Center*

*3. National Institute on Aging*

*4. Dementia.org*

*5. Alzheimers.gov*

*6. Alzheimer's Association*

*7. Cleveland Clinic*

*8. Mayo Clinic*

*9. National Institutes of Health (NIH)*

*10. National Alliance for Caregiving*

Each of these organizations has its helpline on its official website. Thus, whenever you are in a state of dilemma about your loved one's condition, you can always call them and make the necessary inquiries.

## GETTING HELP FOR YOUR LOVED ONE'S MEMORY DETERIORATION

Based on everything we have examined from the first chapter of this book till this point, you will agree that the first and most critical symptom often associated with dementia is the gradual deterioration in the patient's memory. Let's check out some helpful tools to help manage that particular dementia symptom.

- **Memory Screenings**

One of the easiest ways your loved one's dementia condition can get detected quickly is through memory screenings. This screening is a simple and safe type of brain check-up in which a medical expert tests your loved one's memory and thinking skills by asking them to complete a series of questions and tasks within a particular timeframe, usually in less than 10 minutes (Alzheimer's Foundation of America, 2021). Although the findings from this screening will not be enough to make an accurate dementia diagnosis, it still helps detect if your loved one is showcasing signs of mild cognitive impairment and needs a more comprehensive dementia evaluation. With that early detection through memory screening, it will be easier to slow down the rate at which your loved one's memory deteriorates.

The Alzheimer's Foundation of America offers free memory screenings every day, and the best part is that these free screening exercises get conducted virtually (online). All you and your loved one need is a device with a webcam and internet service. Isn't it incredible that your loved one can get such an effective service for free and, most importantly, from the comfort of their home?

- **Music Therapy**

In the previous chapters, we have mentioned and examined several therapy types that you can choose to manage the symptoms of your dementia loved one and slow the progression of their disease. However, that list would only be complete with the inclusion of music therapy.

Research studies have revealed that while people with dementia experience massive changes in different areas of their brains as the disease progresses, their ability to enjoy and react to music remains intact almost until death (Duncan, 2016). Thus, if you play a familiar song right now that your loved one used to love, there is a high possibility that despite their severe memory impairment, they will still remember the lyrics of that song.

Music is such a powerful stimulus that, if used intentionally and appropriately, it can trigger the memories of your loved one, help them restore a part of their identity, and reconnect with reality for some time. In those moments of reconnection, you can see your loved ones being their old selves again. But besides improving memory, music can also improve their psychological and emotional well-being. So take, for instance, your loved one starts exhibiting different aggressive behaviors. At that moment, if you put on a song that got played at their wedding, it will have a calming effect on them because of the happy memories it triggers in their mind and brain. However, the only way your loved one can derive all of these benefits through music therapy is to listen to the songs they truly enjoy. So how do you find tunes that your loved one will most likely enjoy? You can pick several options, like the classics that were popular during your loved one's youth, songs that are connected to specific moments in their lifetime, their favorite hymns from church, or even musicals. It could even be jingles from their favorite TV commercials. Ultimately, what matters the most is for the selected songs to trigger your loved one's memories and evoke the right emotions.

## EMPLOYING PROFESSIONAL SERVICES

While discussing the stages of dementia in Chapter 3, you would remember we emphasized that at the mid and later dementia stages, your loved one starts showcasing unusual symptoms that are too severe for you and other family members to handle alone.

The kind and amount of care your loved one requires goes beyond what you can offer them at home as their primary care-giver (Stephenson, 2022). Hence, as much as you truly want to be the one to take care of your dementia loved one, your best option, at that critical stage, lies in finding the appropriate professional services that can provide them with the best full-time and long-term specialized care.

There are several available professional services for dementia care in the United States. However, the features and functions of these services differ based on cost, length of care, and the dementia stages for which they can provide the best care. Thus, to help you make the best decision for your loved one's condi-tion, we will examine what services and facilities each profes-sional dementia care alternative have to offer.

- **Assisted Living Facilities**

An assisted-living facility is often the first bus stop for dementia patients transitioning into residential care services after spending years at home, receiving family caregiving. However, you should understand that your dementia loved one will only be suitable for this kind of residential facility if their conditions are not at their worse stages. This is because assisted living facilities focus on providing less intensive care than other medical services, so it is important they choose the right resident. An assisted living facility will be perfect for a dementia patient at stages 4 and 5.

Although such a patient is already experiencing symptoms of worsened memory and cognitive impairment as well as several behavioral changes like hallucinations and delusions, they still have significant control over their brain and body. This little control enables them to complete certain daily activities like talking, moving, and eating, though not at the same level as a completely healthy person. At these assisted living homes, your beloved family member can enjoy their own comfortable apartment or a pleasant, shared space with communal amenities such as bathrooms and kitchens and will have access to all of the necessary resources in order for them to be able to live comfortably. Notwithstanding, they get access to several amazing services like 24-hour supervision by a professional healthcare provider, freshly cooked meals, assistance with their personal care, housekeeping, feeding and laundry, adequate security, and support from other on-site staff (National Institute on Aging, 2021). Additionally, your loved one also gets to interact with other dementia patients and participate in fun social and recreational activities specifically designed to improve their cognitive functioning abilities.

In the U. S., the exact housing arrangements and required number of residents in assisted living facilities differ from state to state. However, the good news is that countless agencies specialize in providing state regulations and inspections in assisted living facilities to ensure that there are few to no cases of patient neglect or abuse (Rosenfeld, 2021).

- **Nursing Home Facilities**

In the dementia community, there is a common misconception that nursing homes and assisted living facilities are interchangeable. This presumption is not always true, though. Compared to assisted living facilities, nursing homes offer a higher standard of medical care; they frequently have more qualified staff, more specialized equipment, and treatments, and are subject to state or federal regulations. They offer 24-hour nursing care and medical supervision as well as the different non-drug treatments of dementia that we examined in Chapter 4. Their facilities are designed to provide a safe environment for residents with more advanced forms of dementia.

Healthcare professionals can help guide your loved one through various rehabilitative programs, such as Occupational Therapy and Speech Therapy, Reality Orientation Therapy, and Cognitive Stimulation Therapy. Nevertheless, we must note that before your loved one can get admitted to any nursing home across the U. S., their condition must demand a "nursing home level of care." Thus, when your loved one's condition reaches stages 6 and 7, they become eligible for admission into a nursing home.

- **Hospice**

As much as we might be scared to admit it, dementia is an incurable condition, and no matter how long we manage to slow its progression, it results in death. And just like every average human, your dementia loved one gets more scared of death each day, especially when they are in the critical stages of their condition. Thus, no matter how you and other people try to make them feel better, that fear of death fills their entire body, mind, and soul with a deep sense of loneliness and pain. However, as a primary caregiver, you have the power to ensure that your loved one does not spend the last moments in fear, sorrow, and loneliness. And the only way to make that happen is by providing them with hospice care rather than making them spend their last months in a nursing home or hospital.

At the stage of hospice care, your loved one gets relieved from taking dementia-slowing medications, and the focus switches to providing adequate care to improve their physical, social, emotional, and spiritual well-being. However, this hospice care job does not fall on a single person. Rather, it is under the control of an interdisciplinary team comprising of your loved one's primary physician, social worker, counselor, spiritual leader, licensed nurses, therapist, dietician, and the amazing hospice staff. These experts all come together to design a care plan that will enable your loved one to live their last moments in comfort, grace, fullness, and dignity (Dementia. Org, 2013).

The hospice team also offers services within the comfort of your loved one's home, where you and other family members can be with them. The team also supports the entire family through grief counseling and prepares you emotionally and mentally for the death of your loved one.

Ultimately, we cannot deny that deciding to place your loved one in any of the professional care facilities we just examined is extremely challenging and heartbreaking. However, you must understand that making this crucial decision will go a long way in ensuring that your loved one lives the best way possible.

Employing these professional services also benefits you as the primary caregiver. It reduces the caregiving burden on you and gives a great sense of reassurance, knowing that your loved one is being given the best care in their final moments on earth. Hence, when that time comes for you to decide on handing the care of your loved one to the professionals, remember that you are not neglecting them but trying to improve the quality of their life.

Acknowledge that fact and derive strength and courage from it to make the right choice for your loved one!

# CONCLUSION

 "Self-care is not selfish. You cannot serve from an empty vessel."

— Eleanor Brown

Before you started reading the first chapter of this book, the possibility of achieving an incredible, happy and fulfilling breakthrough in your caregiving journey might have seemed quite far-fetched. However, after exploring the eight knowledge-filled chapters in this book, your mindset, perspectives, and expectations about caregiving have fundamentally transformed. But to refresh our minds, let's do a quick summary of our exploits in each chapter.

We kick-started this adventure by correcting the misconceptions that most people tend to have about dementia, from its causes and types to its risk factors and description as a genetic condition. Then, we went on to explore the different dynamics of dementia from the viewpoints of medical experts and researchers. We also did an in-depth analysis of the ten most common types of dementia, the seven stages of the disease progression, and the available treatment alternatives to slow the progression of your loved one's dementia symptoms.

Having set a solid foundation by exploring those significant areas of dementia, we dove into the core and most crucial parts of our adventure. Firstly, we focused on exploring dementia from the perspective of your loved one. During this exploration, we got to answer some of the essential questions that trouble the minds of every caregiver — What causes your loved one to suddenly transform into someone you barely recognize? Why do they react so violently even when you are solely and desperately trying to help them?

We also described the necessary conditions that enable people with dementia to continue working, driving, and living alone after their diagnosis. As a follow-up, we then identified the best approaches you can take to encourage your loved one when their dementia condition worsens, and they must retire from exercising these three major life activities.

After examining dementia from the perspective of your loved one, we switched to the other side of the spectrum, which focuses on you as the primary caregiver. This book has helped you gain adequate knowledge of what this unpaid but fulfilling job demands from you. In addition, we did a step-by-step breakdown of the emotional and physical burdens you are likely to experience at the different stages of your caregiving journey.

Chapter 7 marked the ultimate climax point in this book. We formulated an effective plan of action that comprises practical steps and strategies with which you can tackle the most critical caregiving, from complex emotional distress like denial and guilt to financial difficulties and how to create a healthier and safe environment for your dementia loved one.

Finally, we wrapped up this exceptional caregiver's guide by providing you with adequate information about the best resources you, as a primary caregiver, can take advantage of to make your job less burdensome. This bonus chapter is my good luck gift to you.

We have done a decent summary of the main areas we explored through the eight chapters of this book. But while we cannot deny that we unpacked a truckload of information in this guide, it might get overwhelming if you try to internalize it all at once. So, it would be best if you take it one step at a time. For example, instead of implementing the seven broad categories of the action plan at once into your and your loved one's daily routine, you should concentrate on one section and gradually incorporate the others when you begin to see productive results or responses from your attempt. Nonetheless, you may be feeling doubtful of yourself after reading through the content of the book. Perhaps, you cannot help but ask yourself — do I truly have what it takes to implement the knowledge from this book and succeed at giving my loved one the best care? What if I fail?

If these questions sound like what is going through your mind, I need you to take a moment to unwind and allow yourself to relax. Although the truth is that you are probably neither a certified medical practitioner nor were you ever prepared for this caregiving role, I assure you that you have everything it takes to succeed on this journey. You are the perfect candidate for this job because you love this patient with all your heart and are determined to improve their quality of life despite the severity of their disease. You are more than set up for success with the knowledge you have acquired from this guide.

Of course, I cannot deny that there will be times when things get dark and challenging, and you will feel like giving up completely. You must fight the temptation to drown yourself in negativity during such moments. Reflecting on the self-care strategies you've learned in this guide and applying them to your daily life are essential to preserving good emotional, mental, and physical health.

Remember that your health and overall well-being matter as much as that of your loved one. And the only way you can deliver the best care to them is if you are in your best physical, mental, and emotional state. To succeed on this journey, you must embrace your sense of purpose as a caregiver and acknowledge that you are dedicating a significant part of your life to caring for your loved one. If you let that mindset guide your every action and decision, I do not doubt that you will easily record immense success in your caregiving journey without getting overwhelmed.

While I might not be there with you physically, I will be cheering and rooting for you and your loved one with hope and confidence that you will make it work, no matter the odds!

If you would like to stay connected, you may want to join our private group to share with other dementia caregivers!

Blessings!

# LEAVE A 1-CLICK REVIEW

## Customer Reviews

★★★★★ 2
5.0 out of 5 stars ▾

| | | |
|---|---|---|
| 5 star | ▓▓▓▓▓▓ | 100% |
| 4 star | | 0% |
| 3 star | | 0% |
| 2 star | | 0% |
| 1 star | | 0% |

See all verified purchase reviews ›

Share your thoughts with other customers

[Write a customer review] ⟵

I would be incredibly thankful if you take just 60-seconds to write a brief review on Amazon, even if it's just a few sentences!

https://amazon.com/review/create-review?asin=1960188003

# ABOUT THE AUTHOR

**Janet G. Cruz**

Janet has studied in the fields of Sociology, Psychology, and Art; she expresses her creativity through writing and visual art.

She started writing to process her feelings after losing her husband to cancer and eventually started publishing her work. She has always been interested in helping others because she believes life is wonderful despite our many trials.

Through her books, she wants to help as many readers as possible by sharing her experiences, knowledge, and thorough research so that other caregivers can have a better quality of life as well.

With this guide, the author wanted to share her experiences in caregiving. She was the primary caregiver of several members of her family (her mother, aunt, and husband) for many years. Her aunt also suffered from dementia and the author knows what it's like to be on both sides of the caregiving spectrum and would like to help other caregivers through her writing.

Janet can be reached at publishing@uconcept.com or via social media:

# BIBLIOGRAPHY

Abrahms, S. (2021). Do You Mind? Meditation for Caregivers. Retrieved From.
https://familycaregivercouncil.com/do-you-mind-meditation-for-caregivers/

Allen, K. (2021). When a Parent Lives Alone and Has Alzheimer's: It Takes a
Village. Retrieved From.
https://www.brightfocus.org/alzheimers/article/when-parent-lives-alone-
and-has-alzheimers-it-takes-village

Alzheimer's Association. (2021). 10 Early Signs and Symptoms of Alzheimer's.
Retrieved From
https://www.alz.org/alzheimers-dementia/10_signs

Alzheimer's Association. (2021). Adult Day Centers. Retrieved From.
https://www.alz.org/help-support/caregiving/care-options/adult-day-centers

Alzheimer's Association. (2021). Caregiver Stress. Retrieved From.
https://www.alz.org/help-support/caregiving/caregiver-health/caregiver-
stress

Alzheimer's Association. (2021). Dementia and Driving. Retrieved From.
https://www.alz.org/help-support/caregiving/safety/dementia-driving

Alzheimer's Association. (2021). In-home Care. Retrieved From.
https://www.alz.org/help-support/caregiving/care-options/in-home-care

Alzheimer's Association. (2021). Is it getting older, or dementia? Retrieved
From.
https://www.alzheimers.org.uk/about-dementia/symptoms-and-diagnosis/
how-dementia-progresses/is-it-getting-older-or-dementia

Alzheimer's Association. (2021). Plan for Your Future. Retrieved From.
https://www.alz.org/help-support/i-have-alz/plan-for-your-future

Alzheimer's Association. (2021). Respite Care. Retrieved From.
https://www.alz.org/help-support/caregiving/care-options/respite-care#:~:
text=Respite%20care%20provides%20caregivers%20a,ability%20to%
20be%20a%20caregiver.

Alzheimer's Association. (2021). Wandering. Retrieved From.
https://www.alz.org/help-support/caregiving/stages-behaviors/wandering#:~:

text=It%20may%20act%20as%20a,or%20other%20outside%20common%20areas.

Alzheimer's Foundation of America. (2022). Alzheimer's & Dementia Facts & Tips. Retrieved From.

https://alzfdn.org/caregiving-resources/facts-tips/

Alzheimer's Society. (2021). How Does Dementia Change a Person's Behavior? Retrieved From.

https://www.alzheimers.org.uk/about-dementia/symptoms-and-diagnosis/symptoms/behaviour-changes

Alzheimer's Society. (2021). Activity groups – for People with Dementia and their Carers. Retrieved From.

https://www.alzheimers.org.uk/get-support/your-dementia-support-services/activity-groups

Alzheimer's Society. (2021). Living Alone as a Person with Dementia. Retrieved From.

https://www.alzheimers.org.uk/get-support/staying-independent/living-alone

Alzheimer's Society. (2021). How To Know When a Person with Dementia Is Nearing the End of their Life. Retrieved From.

https://www.alzheimers.org.uk/get-support/help-dementia-care/recognising-when-someone-reaching-end-their-life

Alzheimer's Society. (2021). Memory loss and dementia. Retrieved From.

https://www.alzheimers.org.uk/about-dementia/symptoms-and-diagnosis/symptoms/memory

Alzheimer's Society of Canada. (2021). Understanding how your Relationship may Change. Retrieved From

https://alzheimer.ca/en/help-support/i-have-friend-or-family-member-who-lives-dementia/understanding-how-your-relationship

Alzheimer's Society. (2021). When Family, Friends or Carers are in Denial about Dementia. Retrieved From.

https://www.alzheimers.org.uk/get-support/help-dementia-care/when-family-friends-carers-denial-about-dementia

American Psychological Association. (2021). Coping with Caregiver Stress and Burden. Retrieved From.

https://www.apa.org/pi/about/publications/caregivers/practice-settings/assessment/tools/stress-burden

A Senior Living Resource. (2022). The Importance of a Daily Routine for Dementia Patients. Retrieved From.
https://www.whereyoulivematters.org/importance-of-routines-for-dementia/

Bhandari, S. (2022). Dementia. Retrieved From.
https://www.webmd.com/alzheimers/types-dementia

Cedars-Sinai. (2020). Myths about Dementia, Alzheimer's and Memory Loss. Retrieved From.
https://www.cedars-sinai.org/blog.html

Christiansen, S. (2021). Dementia Support Groups. Retrieved From.
https://www.verywellhealth.com/best-dementia-support-groups-4843171

Cleveland Clinic. (2021). Brain Overload? 5 Tricks to Stop Feeling So Overwhelmed. Retrieved From.
https://health.clevelandclinic.org/brain-overload-5-tricks-to-stop-feeling-so-overwhelmed/amp/

Cleveland Clinic. (2019). Caregiver Burnout. Retrieved From.
https://my.clevelandclinic.org/health/diseases/9225-caregiver-burnout#:~:text=is%20caregiver%20burnout%3F

DailyCaring Editorial Team. (2016). 8 Ways to Prevent Alzheimer's Wandering. Retrieved From.
https://dailycaring.com/8-ways-to-prevent-alzheimers-wandering/

DailyCaring Editorial Team. (2016). Activities for Dementia: 10 Fun, No-Fail Ideas. Retrieved From.
https://dailycaring.com/activities-for-people-with-dementia-10-fun-no-fail-ideas/

DailyCaring Editorial Team. (2016). This Caregiver Stress Test Helps You Avoid Burnout. Retrieved From.
https://dailycaring.com/whats-your-caregiver-stress-test-score/

Dementia Australia. (2020). Early diagnosis of dementia. Retrieved From.
https://www.dementia.org.au/information/diagnosing-dementia/early-diagnosis-of-dementia#:~:text

Dementia Care Central, (2022). Nursing Homes & Dementia / Alzheimer's | Care Quality, Costs & Financial Assistance. Retrieved From.
https://www.dementiacarecentral.com/nursing-homes/everything-to-know

Dementia.org. (2013). An Introduction to Hospice. Retrieved From.
https://dementia.org/how-hospice-works

Dementia.org. (2013). Causes Of Dementia. Retrieved From.
https://www.dementia.org/causes

Dementia.org. (2014). Does Someone You Know Have Dementia? Retrieved From.
https://www.dementia.org/what-is-dementia

Dementia.org. (2014). Music as Medicine: Music Can Help Dementia Patients. Retrieved From.
https://dementia.org/music-can-help-dementia-patients

Dolgoff, S. (2021). How Stress Can Cause Weight Loss—and What to Do About It. Retrieved From.
https://www.prevention.com/health/mental-health/a37775615/can-stress-cause-weight-loss/

Duncan, A. (2016). A Music Therapist's Perspective on Music and Dementia. Retrieved From.
https://dementia.org/6-ways-music-can-help-manage-dementia

Fold-Martin, P. (2022). Types of Dementia. Retrieved From.
https://www.webmd.com/alzheimers/guide/alzheimers-dementia

Gardner, A. (2021). 7 Stages of Alzheimer's Disease. Retrieved From
https://www.webmd.com/alzheimers/guide/alzheimers-disease-stages

Ghebrai, M. (2021). 23 Best Caregiver Support Groups Online and In-Person. Retrieved From.
https://www.aplaceformom.com/caregiver-resources/articles/caregiver-support-groups

Gilbert, J. (2016). How to Cope With Denial in Dementia. Retrieved From.
https://myhometouch.com/articles/how-to-cope-with-denial-in-dementia

Gupta, S. (2022). What Are the 7 Stages of Dementia? Retrieved From.
https://www.verywellmind.com/the-7-stages-of-dementia-symptoms-and-what-to-expect-6823696

Hallstorm, L. (2022). The 7 Stages of Dementia and Symptoms. Retrieved From
https://www.aplaceformom.com/caregiver-resources/articles/dementia-stages

HealthHub. (2022). Caring for Dementia Patients - Handle Feelings with Care. Retrieved From.
https://www.healthhub.sg/live-healthy/946/caring-for-dementia-patients-handle-feelings-with-care

Heggs, G. (2022). Tips to Reduce The Caregiver Financial Burden. Retrieved

From.
https://dailycaring.com/7-tips-to-reduce-the-caregiver-financial-burden/

Hero Health. (2021). 5 Meditations for Caregivers: Quick Practices to Relieve Stress in 10 minutes or Less. Retrieved From.
https://herohealth.com/blog/caregiving/meditations-for-caregivers/

HelpGuide. (2021). Caregiver Stress and Burnout. Retrieved From.
https://www.helpguide.org/articles/stress/caregiver-stress-and-burnout.htm

Heerema, E. (2021). How to Respond to Combative Behavior in Dementia. Retrieved From.
https://www.verywellhealth.com/how-to-respond-to-combative-behavior-from-dementia-97987

Heerema, E. (2022). Using Reality Orientation in Alzheimer's and Dementia. Retrieved From.
https://www.verywellhealth.com/treating-alzheimers-disease-with-reality-orientation-98682

Hightower, G. (2020). 6 Possible Reasons for Changes in Your Aging Parent's Behavior. Retrieved From.
https://www.homecareassistancearlingtontx.com/why-is-my-older-loved-ones-behavior-changing/

Higuera, V. (2021). 11 Early Signs of Dementia. Retrieved From.
https://www.healthline.com/health/dementia/early-warning-signs#dementia-types

Hobson, G. (2021). Dealing with Dementia Behaviors: Tips for Understanding and Coping. Retrieved From.
https://www.aplaceformom.com/caregiver-resources/articles/dementia-behaviors

Hoshaw, C. (2022). What is Mindfulness? A Simple Practice for Greater Wellbeing. Retrieved From.
https://www.healthline.com/health/mind-body/what-is-mindfulness

Huntsberry-Lett, A. (2022). How to Choose Respite Care for Dementia Patients. Retrieved From.
https://www.agingcare.com/articles/amp/141351

Huzar, T. (2022). What Are The Early Signs Of Dementia? Retrieved From.
https://www.medicalnewstoday.com/articles/324516#early-signs-of-dementia

John Hopkins Medicine. (2020). Dementia Care: Keeping Loved Ones Safe and

Happy at Home. Retrieved From.
https://www.hopkinsmedicine.org/health/wellness-and-prevention/safe-and-happy-at-home

Lifted Team. (2021). What Is Cognitive Stimulation Therapy? Retrieved From.
https://www.liftedcare.com/what-is-cognitive-stimulation-therapy/

Love, K. (2018). Should You Stop Working? Guidance for People Living with Early-Stage Dementia by Marie Marley. Retrieved From.
https://daanow.org/should-you-stop-working-guidance-for-people-living-with-early-stage-dementia/

Marill, M. C. (2022). Is This Normal Aging or Not? Retrieved From.
https://www.webmd.com

Mayo Clinic. (2020). Alzheimer's: Dealing with Family Conflict. Retrieved From.
https://www.mayoclinic.org/diseases-conditions/depression/in-depth/depression/art-20045943

Mayo Clinic. (2021). Alzheimer's and Dementia care: Tips for daily tasks. Retrieved From.
https://www.mayoclinic.org/healthy-lifestyle/caregivers/in-depth/alzheimers-caregiver/art-20047577

Mayo Clinic. (2021). Dementia. Retrieved From.
https://www.mayoclinic.org/diseases-conditions/dementia/symptoms-causes/syc-20352013

Mayo Clinic. (2021). Insomnia. Retrieved From.
https://www.mayoclinic.org/diseases-conditions/insomnia/symptoms-causes/syc-20355167#:~:text=Insomnia%20is%20a%20common%20sleep,tired%20when%20you%20wake%20up.

Mayo Clinic. (2021). Mindfulness Exercises. Retrieved From.
https://www.mayoclinic.org/healthy-lifestyle/consumer-health/in-depth/mindfulness-exercises/art-20046356

Mayo Clinic. (2021). Stress Management. Retrieved From.
https://www.mayoclinic.org/healthy-lifestyle/stress-management/in-depth/caregiver-stress/art-20044784

Melinosky, C. (2022). Which Medicines Treat Dementia? Retrieved From
https://www.webmd.com/alzheimers/guide/medicines-to-treat-dementia

My Life Films. (2021). The Impact Of Dementia On Carers And Family

Members. Retrieved From.
https://mylifefilms.org/dementia-impact-on-carers-and-family-members/
Nail, R. (2022). 10 Types of Dementia. Retrieved From.
https://www.healthline.com/health/types-dementia
National Institute on Aging. (2021). Activities to Do with a Family Member or
Friend Who Has Alzheimer's disease. Retrieved From.
https://www.nia.nih.gov/health/activities-do-family-member-or-friend-who-
has-alzheimers-disease
National Institute on Aging. (2021). Can I Prevent Dementia? Retrieved From.
https://www.alzheimers.gov/life-with-dementia/can-i-prevent-dementia
National Institute on Aging. (2021). Residential Facilities, Assisted Living, and
Nursing Homes. Retrieved From.
https://www.nia.nih.gov/health/residential-facilities-assisted-living-and-nurs
ing-homes
National Institute on Aging. (2021). Tips for Caregivers and Families of People
with Dementia. Retrieved From.
https://www.alzheimers.gov/life-with-dementia/tips-caregivers
National Institute on Aging. (2021). What Is Dementia? Symptoms, Types, and
Diagnosis. Retrieved From.
https://www.nia.nih.gov/health/what-is-dementia
Nelson, A. (2021). Common Challenges Caregivers of Dementia Patients Face.
Retrieved From.
https://www.homehelpershomecare.com/appleton-wi/community-blog/2019/
may/common-challenges-caregivers-of-dementia-patient/
Newman, T. (2020). Medical myths: All about Dementia. Retrieved From
https://www.medicalnewstoday.com/articles/medical-myths-all-about-
dementia
Olsen, E. J. (2021). Lack of sleep: Can it make you sick? Retrieved From.
https://www.mayoclinic.org/diseases-conditions/insomnia/expert-answers/
lack-of-sleep/faq-20057757
Rosenfeld, J. (2021). Can Dementia Patients Live in an Assisted Living Facility?
Retrieved From.
https://www.rosenfeldinjurylawyers.com/news/amp/can-dementia-patients-
live-in-an-assisted-living-facility/
Samuels, C. (2020). 6 Major Health Risks for Dementia Caregivers. Retrieved

From.
https://www.aplaceformom.com/caregiver-resources/articles/health-risks-for-dementia-caregivers

Samuels, C. (2021). What is Reminiscence Therapy for Dementia?
https://www.aplaceformom.com/caregiver-resources/articles/reminiscence-therapy

Sawchuk, C. (2021). Depression (major depressive disorder). Retrieved From.
https://www.mayoclinic.org/diseases-conditions/depression/symptoms-causes/syc-20356007

Sliver Team. (2017). How to Build a Dementia-Friendly Home for Safety & Health. Retrieved From.
https://blog.silvercuisine.com/9-tips-for-a-dementia-friendly-home/#:~:text= Be%20Simple%20and%20Clutter%2DFree,distracting%20to%20individu als%20with%20dementia.

Stephenson, B. (2022). When Should Someone with Dementia Go into a Care Home? Retrieved From.
https://blog.rehabselect.net/when-should-someone-with-dementia-go-into-a-care-home?hs_amp=true

Stringfellow, A. (2019). Activities for Dementia Patients: 50 Tips and Ideas to Keep Patients with Dementia Engaged. Retrieved From.
https://www.seniorlink.com/blog/activities-for-dementia-patients-50-tips-and-ideas-to-keep-patients-with-dementia-engaged

Sutton, J. (2019). What Is Mindfulness? Definition, Benefits & Psychology. Retrieved From.
https://positivepsychology.com/what-is-mindfulness/

Tappana, J. (2020). The Invisible Second Patient: Dementia Caregivers. Retrieved From.
https://aspirecounselingmo.com/blog/the-invisible-second-patient-dementia-caregivers?format=amp

UCSF Health. (2021). Coping Strategies for Vascular Dementia Caregivers. Retrieved From.
https://www.ucsfhealth.org/education/coping-strategies-for-vascular-dementia-caregivers

Unicity Healthcare. (2021). The Effects Alzheimer's Disease Has on Family Members and Caregivers. Retrieved From.

https://unicityhealthcare.com/effects-alzheimers-disease-family-members-caregivers/

Wietza, L. (2021). It's OK to Feel: The Emotional Side of Caregiving. Retrieved From.

https://benrose.org/-/resource-library/family-caregiving/its-ok-to-feel#:~:text=The%20reality%20is%20that%20caregivers,often%20within%20the%20same%20day.

Carter, R. (2011). Family Caregiving Issues and the National Family Caregiver Support Program. Retrieved From.

https://www.cartercenter.org/news/editorials_speeches/rosalynn-carter-committee-on-aging-testimony.html

White, J. (2022). 80 Quotes That Will Resonate With Anyone Who Has Ever Loved Someone With Alzheimer's. Retrieved From.

https://parade.com/1178790/kaitlin-vogel/alzheimers-quotes/

Buechner, C. (2020) 10 Encouraging Quotes for Caregivers to Brighten Your Dat. Retrieved From.

https://www.caringbridge.org/resources/inspirational-quotes-on-caregiving/

Mercree, A. (2020) 10 Encouraging Quotes for Caregivers to Brighten Your Dat. Retrieved From.

https://www.caringbridge.org/resources/inspirational-quotes-on-caregiving/

Mother Teresa. Mother Teresa Quotes. Retrieve From.

https://www.goodreads.com/author/quotes/838305.Mother_Teresa

Lama, D. 15 Inspirational Quotes for Caregivers. Retrieve From.

https://www.alegrecare.com/single-post/inspirational-quotes-for-caregivers

Walker, T. (2020) 10 Encouraging Quotes for Caregivers to Brighten Your Dat. Retrieved From.

https://www.caringbridge.org/resources/inspirational-quotes-on-caregiving/

Made in the USA
Columbia, SC
17 March 2024

33175904R00107